Ft. Detroit
Ft. Deposit
Ft. Defiance
St. Marys
Piqua
Xenia
Ft. Hamilton
Ft. Washingto
(Cincinnati)
LITTLE MIAMI
RIVER

LITTLE TURTLE

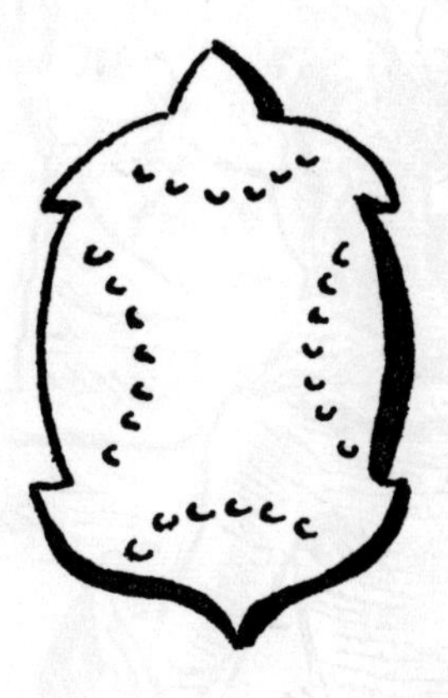

LITTLE TURTLE
Miami Chief

By Jean Carper & Grace L. Dickerson

Illustrated by
Grace Leslie Dickerson

ALBERT WHITMAN & COMPANY
Chicago Illinois

L. C. Card 59–14392

Published simultaneously in the Dominion of Canada by George J. McLeod, Limited, Toronto. Printed in the U.S.A.

CONTENTS

Chapter I
EXCITING MESSAGE

It was early April, 1777, when five British soldiers landed at the Indian village of Kekionga. Their arrival excited the villagers.

Indians ran from wigwams. Traders left their cabins. Everyone crowded along the banks of the Maumee River to see the soldiers come ashore.

"Stand back! Stand back!" commanded a soldier in a crimson coat and white trousers.

The crowd eased back, leaving a good-sized opening for the soldiers.

Straining to see over the many heads was a young chief, Little Turtle of the Miamis. He was not a very powerful chief. He was leader of a small village twenty miles northwest of Kekionga and had come to the large village to trade furs.

Little Turtle saw the soldiers unload a pudgy six pound cannon. He had never seen one before.

The soldiers wheeled the cannon out into the dirt street. One soldier rammed powder in the barrel. Another lit a fuse, then ran backward. The cannon roared into faraway trees.

Squaws and even warriors were terrified. Some screamed. Some fell to the ground, trying to hide.

Little Turtle was slightly frightened too, but he stood firm. He stared at the smoking gun.

The soldiers laughed loudly.

"It is a great gun that makes thunder," said a soldier in the Miami language. "It can kill many men. It can hit a target far away. But do not be afraid. Only our enemies must fear it."

Several times the soldiers fired the cannon. Each time the Indians shuddered.

Finally a soldier held up his hand for silence. "We have a very important message for you from the great white father at Fort Detroit. Let us meet your greatest chief. Then let us all sit together in council."

Two old chiefs, Pecanne and LeGris of the Miamis, came forward to greet the soldiers. They all headed for the council house. Little Turtle and the lesser chiefs fell in behind. Warriors followed.

The village's main street took them by fifty cabins that belonged to fur traders. Beyond the street were clusters of wigwams. To the west and north was a wilderness—thick with forests of birch, elm, and oak. To the south were fields where the Indians would plant corn—as soon as the white oak leaf was as big as a mouse's ear, they said. Then the fields would stretch green for miles.

Kekionga, where Fort Wayne, Indiana, now stands, had been the grand capital of the Miami Indians for centuries. The village was also the trading center of the Midwest. It sat at the crux of three rivers. There the St. Joseph and St. Marys form the big Maumee that flows northeast into Lake Erie.

At the far end of the village, the group entered a long, crudely built council house. Chief LeGris lit the council fire and welcomed the soldiers. Little Turtle sat crosslegged beside LeGris.

Old warriors sat in front, younger ones in back. All warriors could attend the council, but only the bravest could speak.

A soldier stood up. "You know that for many seasons your white brothers have been fighting a war to the east far over the mountains." He was speaking of the American Revolutionary War.

"With the thunder-guns such as we have shown you, we shall kill our enemy, the Americans. But our enemy is also your enemy. The American rebels have been moving across the mountains. They build their wigwams on your hunting grounds in Kentucky. They chase your food away. You cannot go there to hunt and fish as your fathers did."

A few warriors grunted.

"My brothers, we English are your friends. Our great white father wants to help you keep your land."

Little Turtle set his jaw. He was suspicious of all white men, especially the British. He had learned long ago that few white men wanted to help his people. He waited anxiously for the soldier's next words.

"Your great white father at Fort Detroit sends you an important message. He wants to help you bring in many scalps of the white men who are taking your land. He will give you much ammunition, guns, blankets, whiskey and silver earrings for the white scalps you bring him."

Young warriors grew excited. One who wore the prized eagle feather in his hair stood up. "Our British brother speaks the truth. It is wise that we take war parties beyond the Ohio River and bring many scalps to our great white father."

Many warriors agreed.

Little Turtle was troubled. He knew the soldier spoke with a false tongue. The British wanted the Indians to help kill the Americans. That way, the Indians would then be helping the British.

Little Turtle decided to speak. He stood up very straight. He was not small as one might think from his name. Nor was he tall—only 5 feet, 10 inches. But everyone thought he was much taller. Years later when American soldiers met him on the battlefield they swore he was at least 6 feet, 4 inches tall. He seemed to tower over everyone.

His shoulders were wide and his arms and legs were hard with muscle. In contrast, his face was gentle with molded features like smooth sculpture. But his most striking feature was his small black eyes. They were piercing and commanded attention.

He began to speak slowly, as always, and everyone became still.

"My brothers, it is right that we should take scalps of

our white enemies in Kentucky. But we do not need our British friends to tell us this.

"They do not wish to help us. They only wish us to kill their enemies for them. It is right we should kill our enemies to keep our land. But it is not right we should kill them just to take scalps to the great white father so he will give us many presents."

One soldier whispered to another, "That Indian's very smart. Too smart for an Indian."

Proud warriors agreed with Little Turtle. Those who were greedy for the presents from the British said nothing.

The soldier who had spoken, got back up quickly. "My brothers." His voice was soothing. "This chief does not have to bring his scalps to the great white father. But if you bring yours, here are some presents you will receive."

The soldier passed out many gaudy blankets, trinkets and bottles of rum. The warriors took them eagerly. The council was over.

Outside old Chief LeGris came up to Little Turtle. "My son, I feel as you do. But it is the only way for us to keep our land. Our warriors are lazy. If these presents will send warriors to Kentucky, let them go. If it will help drive the settlers off our land, it is a good thing."

Little Turtle looked into the withered face of LeGris. "Yes, many war parties will set out now. I, too, shall start with one when the sun rises. It is what I want—because it will save our land. But I am a proud warrior. I will never sell my scalps to the great white father."

Little Turtle turned abruptly and vanished into the forests.

LeGris watched him. "He is very young with strange ideas," muttered the old chief. "But he is a good chief to his people."

Chapter II

A GAME OF WAR

Little Turtle had always been strong-willed.

His mother said he was like the men of her tribe, the Mohicans. They were quiet; but they were strong and crafty fighters, always able to trick an enemy.

Little Turtle's father, old Chief Acquenacke, never understood his son. They were so different. Acquenacke was built like a big bear. He laughed a lot and told long thrilling stories around the campfire. One of his favorite tales was how Little Turtle got his name.

"My son," the old chief would chuckle, "you were such a tiny baby that all the squaws came just to stare at you. One said, 'You should name him after the painted terrapin turtle. It never grows larger than a squaw's hand!' So we did, and now look at you, son. You have outgrown your name!"

Little Turtle always smiled politely at his father's old tale. But he worried about his father. He did not feel his father was as serious as a chief should be. Acquenacke lolled about the fire, laughing and drinking white man's whiskey. His face would get red and he would stagger into the wigwam to sleep. This disgusted Little Turtle. Even when he was a man he had nothing to do with white man's liquor.

Little Turtle was born in 1751. As a boy, he could hit a rabbit square between the eyes with a bow and arrow. He could outrun everyone in the village, including strong warriors.

When he was twelve he bought a musket with beaver furs he had caught during the winter. He took the gun completely apart, then put it back together again just to see how it worked. He practiced shooting until he became an excellent marksman.

Other boys his age admired his skill, but they felt uneasy around him. He seemed so self-assured. They often made foolish mistakes.

Little Turtle noticed they grew timid when he talked to them. He even felt some were afraid of him. They always listened respectfully to what he said. When he made a joke, they smiled uncertainly and became embarrassed. When he talked earnestly, they did not seem to understand.

Little Turtle found himself often with no one to talk to. So when he was still very young he began a curious habit that he practiced all his life.

At night when he lay in the darkness of his wigwam he could hear the wind ripping through the trees or tearing at the flap on the wigwam door. He listened very carefully. He began to imagine the wind was speaking to him. He was sure it knew many things and that by listening he could learn all its secrets.

Little Turtle learned about war quite easily. To be a warrior was the dream of every Indian boy.

The Miamis carefully drilled their boys for war. There were no schools to learn reading and writing. But there were classes in something much more important to them—how to fight. Their lives depended on how well they learned.

The sessions were strenuous, but Little Turtle liked them. And it was soon evident he would be a good warrior.

One day the boys fought a mock battle. They divided into two groups and Little Turtle was chosen war chief of one.

The boys huddled around him and he told them his war plan. They agreed. Then according to custom, he aroused his warriors to battle. He jumped up onto a stump and said, "Brothers, we shall wipe out the enemy!" He pointed to the boys who were filing down the bumpy path to the west.

Little Turtle looked down on his warriors. "Come," he commanded as he sprang to the ground. He did not follow the enemy. He led his men in the opposite direction, up over a small hill. Then he cut sharply to the south and proceeded all the way to the other side of a lake.

"Here we must wait," he said and sat down. He concealed his men so they could watch the enemy across the lake.

After 15 minutes some of the boys grumbled. One, half Little Turtle's size urged, "Let's come around from behind them and attack."

Little Turtle eyed him. "One does not question a war chief."

Nevertheless, the small boy crawled between the trees and out into the open. Little Turtle grabbed his ankle and pulled his leg from under him. He fell on his stomach.

The boy jumped up, glared at Little Turtle and started to walk away. Little Turtle grabbed him by the arm, twirled him around and slapped him hard on the cheek. "Sit down and wait. You will spoil our plan," he said.

Trembling, the little boy sat down.

In the meantime the other war chief had led his men in the direction Little Turtle had taken. Little Turtle had concealed his cutoff to the south so well, the chief could not find him. The enemy doubled back and explored all the land in the opposite direction. Finally, the chief flopped down in a small clearing. The others squatted around him.

Little Turtle quickly moved his men around the lake and surrounded the enemy. His band swooped down and pinned the enemy boys to the ground.

Little Turtle's father had been watching. "You would have massacred them all!" he cried. "You were clever to wait until you could surprise the enemy. You may even be a war chief one day." He put his hand on Little Turtle's shoulder. For the first time Little Turtle felt close to his father.

That night Little Turtle lay in his quiet, dark wigwam. He was excited he had won the battle, but he was ashamed he had slapped the little boy. He remembered how the boy had trembled. Little Turtle felt sorry for him.

Still the boy was very wrong. He had to learn to obey. If he didn't he might be killed. War was not a game for boys, but a serious part of their lives.

Little Turtle waited for an answer from the wind. He could hear it grumbling in the trees behind the wigwam. Then, suddenly, it softened and slid over the wigwam like a huge comforting hand.

Little Turtle understood. The wind spoke a language only he could understand. But he knew it had said, "You were right. And your father was right. For this night I tell you, one day you will be a famous war chief."

Little Turtle believed the wind. He rolled up in his bearskin and fell peacefully asleep. He never doubted himself again.

He was not even surprised that his tribe chose him chief when his father died. To choose him was very unusual. He could not inherit the leadership because according to custom he belonged to his mother's family. Besides he was only twenty, the youngest chief the tribe had ever had. But everyone said, "He is clever like the fox and swift like the deer. He will make a wise chief."

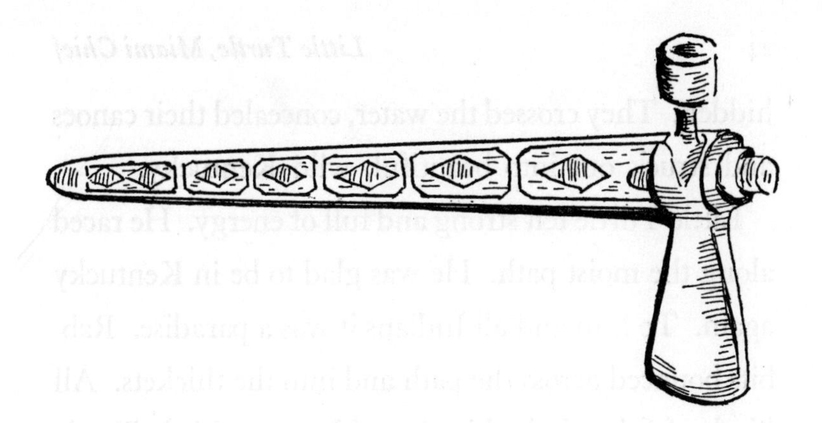

Chapter III

OFF ON A KENTUCKY RAID

After the British soldiers left their message at Kekionga they moved on to other villages.

Little Turtle, as he had promised, set out on a war party the next day. The warriors didn't carry packs or blankets—only guns. They hunted for food along the way.

They followed paths that had been cut through the wilderness by other raiding parties. In several days they reached the Ohio River where their canoes were hidden. They crossed the water, concealed their canoes and struck out into beautiful, wild Kentucky.

Little Turtle felt strong and full of energy. He raced along the moist path. He was glad to be in Kentucky again. To him and all Indians it was a paradise. Rabbits bounced across the path and into the thickets. All kinds of fish splashed in the cold water. Little Turtle could catch a fish with his bare hands.

After several miles in the woods, Little Turtle drew close to a clearing. From a small hill he looked down on a lonely cabin. He ordered his men to approach slowly and surround the cabin. "A new one," commented a brave. "They are planting in the fields," replied Little Turtle.

The warriors crept so close they could smell the newly turned earth. They saw the farmer pushing his plow and his wife tagging behind dropping seed into the furrow.

Two Indians aimed long muskets and fired. The man and his wife dropped. The warriors scrambled

over the brush and then quickly took their scalps.

Little Turtle with other warriors ran to search and burn the cabin.

"Look upstairs," ordered Little Turtle and a brave scampered into the loft.

Little Turtle heard a shrill scream. He dashed up into the loft. The warrior was leaning over a small bed. He was about to bring his tomahawk down on a girl, about four years old. Little Turtle saw the terror on the child's face.

He snatched the child from the path of the warrior's club. With his other hand he hit the warrior hard in the mouth. The warrior fell back against the rough wall.

"Has it come to this?" demanded Little Turtle. "Do you now take the scalps of helpless children. It would disgrace a Miami warrior to hang a child's scalp in the council house."

"But the golden hair will bring many presents from the great white father," the warrior whimpered.

Little Turtle reached over and plucked the eagle feather from the warrior's scalp lock. "You are no longer a warrior. No warrior who ever comes with Little Turtle on a war party will take the hair of children."

A mixture of fear and shame came into the warrior's eyes.

"You will be given back the eagle feather when you prove you can wear it proudly."

Little Turtle gently handed the little girl to the warrior. "She is now yours. Take her back to the village and adopt her as your own. You shall see no harm comes to her."

The warrior knew Little Turtle meant what he said.

They both climbed down from the loft and went into the yard. Other warriors set torches to the cabin. Soon it was blazing.

Little Turtle and his war party fled into the woods.

The smoke from the burning cabin rose high into the sky for settlers all around to see.

Little Turtle had been on many raids before. But he felt that this time, a new, vicious war had been declared between his people and the white settlers. It would not end until one of them had been beaten.

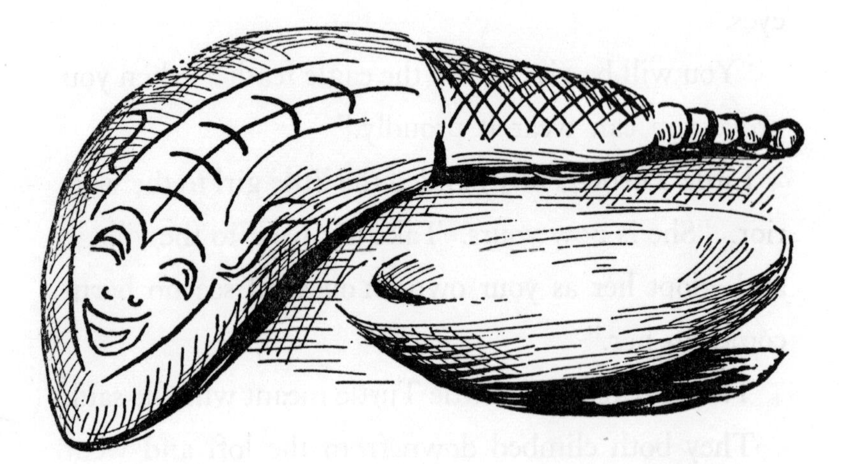

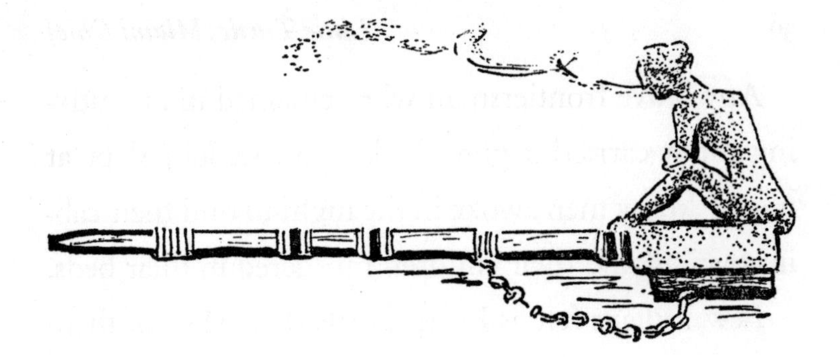

Chapter IV

TERROR ON THE FRONTIER

By the summer of 1777, settlers below the Ohio River were paralyzed with fear of Indian raids. Death was always in the air. It hovered close over the cabins like a hungry vulture. No one knew when it would swoop down.

The fields were bare because no one dared to plant. Nor could they venture into the woods to hunt food. In most settlements the pioneers built a stockade and locked themselves in. Still they suffered almost nightly attacks.

Any brave frontiersman who remained in an outlying cabin carried a gun all day and seldom slept at night. Many men awoke in the night to find their cabins blazing and their children murdered in their beds.

Few Indians felt as Little Turtle did. Most of them were ruthless. They took many children's scalps to sell to the great white father at Fort Detroit.

This great white father was the most hated man in frontier history. His correct name was Henry Hamilton, British Lieutenant Governor in North America. Frontiersmen called him the "hair-buyer" and snarled when they spoke his name.

Helpless Kentucky farmers begged the federal government for protection. Many packed up and fled back to the East.

The new government was not able to protect the settlers. It was still fighting the Revolutionary War.

Finally George Rogers Clark, a settler at Harrodsburg, Kentucky, took action. He felt an army could smash British forts. Then the Indians, with no one to pay for scalps, would quiet down. Clark persuaded Patrick Henry in Virginia to outfit an expedition against the British in the Midwest.

With 175 men who called themselves Long-Knives, Clark took British Forts Kaskaskia and Vincennes. "Hair-buyer" Hamilton packed up his army and came to Vincennes to fight Clark. There Clark captured Hamilton and sent him back to England.

Clark seized one fort after another—all but the most important one, Fort Detroit.

With Hamilton gone, settlers hoped the dreadful Indian attacks would end. Instead they became worse. A new commander who replaced Hamilton still bought scalps from the warriors.

By 1780 Americans along the Kentucky border still lived in constant fear.

Frantic pioneers began asking each other, "Will we ever be rid of these red devils?" They always got the same answer, "Not until someone marches to Fort Detroit to clean out the British murderers."

But all pioneers agreed, "A man like that would have to have the courage of a wildcat."

Was there anyone like that?

A reckless, young colonel at Fort Vincennes was looking for fame. His name was Auguste LaBalme. One night at the Old Yellow Tavern where he drank with his friends he boasted, "Well, I may just lead that army to Fort Detroit myself." A few men laughed.

The young colonel's face reddened. He jumped up, knocking his chair behind him. "Who's going with me? Come on, men! You're always bragging you're brave as all get out. Here's your chance to prove it."

One man said, "Why, I reckon the young coyote means it. Sure, I'll go with you."

Thirty men clustered around the colonel. "When do we get started, colonel?"

"Soon as we round up some more men." LaBalme stomped out of the tavern.

In October, 1780, sixty men in dirty buckskin left Fort Vincennes and headed up the Wabash River. Reinforcements were to join them at the Indian village of Ouiatenon (now Lafayette, Indiana).

When the army reached Ouiatenon, the Indians had fled. LaBalme's spirits soared. "These Indians aren't so brave. Kekionga is right in our path to Detroit. We'll stop there and give them a right good scare as soon as our reinforcements get here from Pennsylvania."

For twelve days, LaBalme waited, but the reinforcements did not come. He could wait no longer. He feared Indians at Kekionga would learn of his approach and ambush him.

LaBalme's men crept through the woods like silent panthers. Not a soul at Kekionga knew they were coming.

Chapter V

SETTLERS' REVENGE

At one o'clock, on the afternoon of November 2, 1780, Colonel LaBalme's army was an hour away from Kekionga. The advancing soldiers must have been unbelievably quiet, for their presence had not been detected by the Indians.

At this moment Little Turtle was striding through the village toward his sister's home. His legs were wrapped in deerskin leggings to keep out the chill November wind. But the sun, tipped toward the west, felt warm on the back of his neck.

As he made his way among the wigwams, he smiled a little at squaws who were lazily stirring corn and beans in huge iron kettles. He dodged in and out among laughing children who chased around tents playing hide and seek. Except for the children's giggles, the village was quiet and half deserted. Nearly all the men had left early in the morning to hunt in nearby forests.

Little Turtle entered a well built French cabin at the east end of the village. Here his sister, Tacumwah, lived. Her husband was a French trader who lived like an Indian. He led many war parties against the Americans. He had been with Blackfish, the Shawnee chief when he captured Daniel Boone.

"My brother," Tacumwah laid down the deerskin shirt she was sewing and rose to greet Little Turtle. She was pleased to see him.

"Is Beaubien here?" asked Little Turtle.

"No, he and Peshewa are hunting. But stay and wait for them, won't you," she insisted. "Sit down.

Let me get you some raccoon I have just roasted."

"Of course," Little Turtle agreed. He was not hungry. He had eaten raccoon just before he left home. But an Indian never refused to eat. It was very bad manners.

In a few minutes Tacumwah handed Little Turtle a wooden bowl filled with steaming chunks of raccoon. Little Turtle looked gently up at the long slim face of his sister. She was not like other squaws who seemed stupid. He liked her because she was shrewd and cunning like a warrior.

Little Turtle did not mind waiting for Beaubien. He was glad to have a chance to talk to his sister. He pushed his legs far under the table. Absently, he chewed on a meaty raccoon leg.

Suddenly, the thick quiet that hung over the village was shattered by several braves clamoring through the streets. "Run for your lives! The Long-Knives are coming!" Little Turtle raced out the door and grabbed a warrior by the arm. "What are you yelling about?"

The warrior gasped. "There's not much time. We were hunting and spotted a deer at the top of a hill. We looked down and saw this whole army coming around the hill toward us."

"How many?" Little Turtle demanded.

"Hundreds!" It was an hysterical guess. "We've got to get out of here." He tore loose from Little Turtle's grip and ran on down the street screaming, "Run! An army is coming!"

Kekionga, so peaceful a few minutes ago, was now confusion. The streets were teeming with terrified squaws, carrying and dragging their children into the nearby forest. Many headed northwest and could be heard splashing across the shallow St. Joseph River.

Little Turtle quickly decided there was nothing to do but flee also. The men were scattered and at the moment he could not gather a force. His blood was raging, but his brain was calm. The time to fight would come later. His next thought was of his sister.

"Tacumwah!" She was already at his side. Together they escaped over the river and into the safety of the dense forest.

An instant later, Colonel LaBalme's men poured into the village. To their surprise and disappointment they found the village deserted. The only sign of human life were kettles of beans and corn steaming over the fires.

Colonel LaBalme then did something very foolish. He turned his men loose to plunder the village. These rowdy men who had lived so many days in the forest like wild animals now behaved like wild animals. They had been cheated out of a fight. They had to have some kind of revenge.

They smashed open warehouses that belonged to French traders and dragged out their goods. They helped themselves to corn and beans and everything else they could lay their hands on.

Colonel LaBalme headed directly to the warehouse of Beaubien, Little Turtle's brother-in-law. LaBalme had long planned to rob Beaubien's storehouse. In his pocket LaBalme carried a letter that listed the wealthy contents of the storehouse as "A thousand weight of powder and lead and in proportion, arms, blankets, cloth and shirts."

Inside the storehouse, LaBalme found an old man, unable to run. He had been left behind to guard the storehouse. In a shaky voice the old man begged the colonel to leave the goods alone. "Please, sir, Mr. Beaubien won't like it one bit."

"Well, now that's too bad," the young colonel drawled and spat on the dirt floor. "We don't like the way Beaubien and his savages come to Kentucky and murder our women and children either." He shoved the old man aside. "Come on men! Take as much stuff as we can carry away."

For a couple of hours LaBalme's men loaded the loot on wagons. Then almost as quickly as it came, the army left the village and headed west. After a few miles they found an open space on the banks of a small stream called the Aboite, and made camp.

"Those savages ran like scared rabbits. We don't have to worry about them for a while," LaBalme told his men. The soldiers built their fires, cooked their suppers and lay down on their blankets.

As soon as the Indians were sure it was safe, they returned to Kekionga. Beaubien was furious when he saw that they had plundered his storehouse. "We're not going to stand for this," he screamed. "I'm going to call a council to decide what to do."

Under Beaubien, the council met.

He pleaded with the warriors to attack the camp. "Rise up and revenge yourselves! Are you afraid? See how the enemy flings your weakness back in your face by camping so close. He is like a brazen wildcat who licks his chops in front of you after he has devoured your children."

Beaubien did not move the warriors. They were reluctant. After all, they army had not really harmed them. Their squaws and children were still alive, their wigwams standing. Beaubien was the only one harmed. Why should they risk their lives to avenge him?

No, it was clear a mere cry for revenge would not arouse these braves. It would take a powerful blow to their pride as warriors. It was at this crucial moment that Little Turtle delivered that blow.

When it seemed hopeless for Beaubien to stir the tribesmen, Little Turtle saw his chance. It was his duty to avenge his brother-in-law. Moreover it was his destiny to defend his people against the white invaders. Now was the time to begin!

Like a powerful tree, quavering in a storm, Little Turtle stood before his indifferent kinsfolk. His words which had always been like a slow steady breeze, now whipped around the men like a whirlwind. The warriors were stunned. Some thought he was mad. Some thought another spirit had captured his body. They listened intently.

Little Turtle insulted them and shamed them. Lastly, he appealed to their honor and pride as Miami warriors. "My brothers, this is our land, yours and mine. It belonged to your fathers, your grandfathers, your great grandfathers and his fathers before that, ever since time immemorial. Do I speak the truth?"

"Yes, Yes!"

"We have owned our beautiful Kekionga on the three waters ever since we can remember. Am I right?"

"Yes."

"Now these whites come like great hunters and we are like wild turkeys that squawk and flutter into the underbrush. And the white men will not stop. They will chase us westward across the great prairies and we will run in flocks. But we shall not escape them. They will hunt us down and drive us into faraway waters. Would you have this?"

"No!" a cry of outrage arose. Fire glowed in their black eyes.

Little Turtle's eyes were hard and narrow. His voice was strained and hushed. Each warrior had to lean for-

"Surely the warriors are in position by now," thought Little Turtle. "Perhaps a minute more? No, I will wait no longer. I will become a war chief now or never."

Little Turtle rose on his strong knees and opened his mouth wide. Deep from his throat came a hideous cry. It froze the blood of the sleepy soldiers.

Bewildered sentries turned to shoot but were thrown to the ground by bullets ripping across their chests. Dazed soldiers jumped up and fumbled for their guns. Most of them were shot before they could fire.

Colonel LaBalme staggered to his feet and stared into the face of Little Turtle. Little Turtle brought his tomahawk down hard. LaBalme crumpled at Little Turtle's feet.

In a few minutes the massacre was over. Little Turtle surveyed the patch of bodies. There must be at least fifty, maybe more, he thought. As far as he could tell only four or five of his own warriors were dead.

On the far side of the clearing Little Turtle noticed

two warriors struggling with a lone survivor. Time and again the soldier beat off his assailants. He wouldn't die. Finally Little Turtle shouted, "Let him live. He is a brave man." This fighting soldier became a prisoner and the only one to live through the LaBalme massacre.

Standing alone, Little Turtle observed the shadowy forms of warriors bending down here and there to take scalps. "These Long-Knives should not have come to our land," murmured Little Turtle. "But it is right they should die. Just as it is right the fox should kill the rabbit and the rabbit should kill the mouse. It is the law of nature and war. It will never change."

Little Turtle removed the scalping knife from his belt. He stooped and swiftly cut off the young colonel's black hair and hung it over his belt. The conquering war chief turned on his heel and melted into the darkness. Bounding after him were joyous warriors dragging along the one prisoner.

Outside the village the victorious Indians set up a

terrific howl. This meant they had brought back many scalps. Those in the village returned the cry. Several times the warriors and villagers exchanged the weird cries. It was a victory ritual.

Squaws hurried to prepare a magnificent feast for the victors. When Little Turtle appeared everyone shouted, "He is a war chief! He is a war chief!" They would not let him alone until he had acted out the massacre several times.

Then the squaws cried, "Let's have the prisoner! Let him run the gauntlet. We shall see if he is really brave."

The prisoner was brought out and stripped of his clothes while savages lined up in two rows. When the naked soldier saw his captors, armed with clubs, stones and sticks, he was afraid. But he had no choice. If he didn't run, they would kill him for a coward.

He took a deep breath and dashed head first through his tormentors. They beat his back with sticks. They tried to knock him down. Once he stumbled but he bounced back up and continued the path of torture.

At the end of the line were the squaws who were the meanest of all. They spat on him and pounded his head with stones. At last, exhausted he reached the end and collapsed. But he passed the test and was allowed to live. Several days later warriors took him to Canada and sold him to the British.

The celebration lasted all night. The sky was alive with sounds of joy and drums, beating out the heavy pulse of a nation still very much alive. The next morning many Indians were lying wherever they had fallen, some drunk, others exhausted.

Little Turtle was up early. He felt fresh and strong in his new glory as a war chief.

He knew the white settlers would hear of the soldiers' massacre. He knew, too, they would hear the name of Little Turtle, a new war chief who would not give up his land without a fight.

Chapter VII

YEAR OF BLOOD—1782

In October, 1781, Lord Cornwallis surrendered at Yorktown. The long fight for independence was over. In the strip of colonies along the ocean, the rejoicing, like that famous "shot" that began the war, was heard 'round the world.

But the cheering that came up out of that strange, inland part of the new nation was enough to deafen the world.

Weary frontiersmen had been plagued so long by

the English and the Indians. Now the hated English would go home. The feared savages would stay far away, north of the Ohio River. Settlers could live like human beings instead of like hunted animals. With these hopes all the frontier heaved a tremendous sigh of relief and looked to better days ahead.

But what of the Indians? What did they think of England's defeat? With their ally gone and without arms and payment for scalps, would the Indians end their raids on outlying settlements? Would they retire quietly behind the border of the Ohio River?

As it turned out, England did not pull out of America immediately following the war. For many years she kept forts in the Midwest and continued to urge the Indians against the Americans.

Even without British encouragement, intelligent Indian leaders were quick to size up the situation after the war. They knew that more and more Americans would now flow westward, covering the land like a flood. They knew also that if they were to hold back this influx, they must strike hard at all the pioneers.

Consequently, the end of the Revolution, instead of bringing peace as settlers expected, brought more bloodshed than ever. The aftermath was so horrible that 1782 went down in Kentucky history as the "Year of Blood."

Both red men and white were responsible for that terrible year. They committed two of pioneer history's worst atrocities.

All over what are now Ohio and Indiana, Indians buzzed like flies, meeting here and there. Each war chief may have had war plans of his own, but he was willing to hear other chiefs. Since the Miamis were an influential tribe, they often called councils at Kekionga.

At these sessions Little Turtle was hailed as a new war chief. Famous old war chiefs from the Shawnees, Wyandots, and Delawares had heard how Little Turtle wiped out LaBalme and his men. Now they listened to Little Turtle's suggestions with a new respect. Even the two most important Miami chiefs, Pecanne and

LeGris, insisted that Little Turtle sit next to them in the council house.

It was during one such council in March that Little Turtle heard of the most hideous crime white men ever committed against the Indians.

Pecanne had just begun to speak when a breathless messenger from the Delawares pushed his way past the guard and burst into the council house.

"What do you want?" asked Little Turtle harshly. "What is so important you dare interrupt the great Chief Pecanne at the council fire?"

"I have a message of horror that will make your blood run cold as the icy creek and your spine shiver like a sapling in the wind," the messenger answered.

"Speak!" commanded Pecanne.

The messenger nervously began his story. At first his words tumbled out haphazardly. "My people in Ohio—100 of them are dead—murdered by the Long-Knives," he stuttered. As he calmed down, the story unraveled in all its gory details.

An army of 100 men under Colonel David Williamson had crossed into Ohio from Fort Pitt to punish some Wyandots who had been raiding settlers. While seeking the culprits the army came upon a group of peaceful Delawares husking corn. The Delawares, known as Moravians, were Christian converts. They were not only harmless, but trusting and friendly.

They smiled at the soldiers and offered them corn as the white man's God said they should do. When the soldiers asked for their guns and tomahawks, they handed them over like innocent, trusting children. The white men said they would look after their Indian brothers.

Without a spark of distrust the Moravian men, women and children trailed the soldiers into a village. When Colonel Williamson saw them he had their hands bound. He tossed them into cabins, women and children in one hut, the men in another. The Indians were completely bewildered.

While they puzzled their predicament, Colonel Williamson decided their fate. "What shall we do with the red devils?" he asked his men. "Kill them?"

Without hesitation the soldiers voted to kill their Indian "brothers."

At sunup the soldiers boldly burst into the cabins. They had nothing to fear. All hands lay helpless behind the Indians' backs. Even the hands of the tiniest children who huddled against their mothers, were bound.

The prisoners in both cabins pleaded silently with their eyes. It was no use. The soldiers removed their knives from their belts. Suddenly, all together the captives began to pray in low whispers, their heads pointed toward heaven. A shriveled old man could be heard above the others, "Forgive them. They know not what they do."

These words should have sent the soldiers from the cabin in deep shame. Instead the humble words inflamed them.

"Quick! Let's shut them up!" roared one soldier.

They fell upon the prisoners with knives and tomahawks. The victims prayed until the very last, when they tumbled to the floor, their lips forever silent. Only the little children screamed when they felt the white man's blade at their throats. Within a few minutes even their screams died away.

A ghostly silence entered the cabins. On bloodstained floors were the mangled bodies of forty men, twenty women and thirty-four children. Without a word to each other, the murderous soldiers stomped out of the cabins and down to the river to scrub the blood from their hands.

This slaughter enraged the Indians of all tribes. By the time word spread from village to village, all Indians were up in arms and ready for revenge.

What was the settlers' reaction to the hideous butchery?

Colonel Williamson and his men were not in disgrace. On the contrary they were heroes. Settlers weren't indignant. They were pleased. The massacre raised pioneer spirits so high that they got up another expedition. The new expedition's battle cry was: "Kill every Indian in sight."

With this goal, about 500 men under Colonel William Crawford bustled out of Fort Pitt and headed toward the villages of the Delawares and Wyandots on the Sandusky River.

This time the Indians were ready for revenge. Angry warriors waited for Colonel Crawford's army as it curled through the wilderness like a monstrous snake. With a whoop, the Indians pounced and deftly wiped out most of the army. But Colonel Crawford was not allowed to die. He was to be the object of the Indians' revenge. He was to be a human sacrifice for the lives of the Christian Delawares. Colonel Crawford was bound and taken to one of the villages where Indians had gathered.

The colonel's face was blackened with charcoal. This meant he was condemned to die. Next he was stripped of his clothes. Jeers of approval went up as two strong warriors led the doomed colonel to a stake. They tied him to one end of a rope, then fastened the other end to the stake.

Now the torture began. Warriors and squaws and children converged on the colonel and beat him with sticks. Some warriors lit torches and poked them into the colonel's face.

After teasing him for some time they let the flames sear his flesh. His shrieks pierced the sky. At last, the colonel collapsed and died.

Indians who saw the colonel burned at the stake talked about it for years. Those who had not seen it, soon heard about it from swift messengers. Everyone was elated! To the Indians it was supreme justice that this man should pay for the murder of the Delawares.

Little Turtle was thrilled by the victory. If the Indians could wipe out a force of 500, perhaps they would be able to keep the white man out. His self-confidence zoomed. He believed the Indian race was still a great nation and would prove it.

Other chiefs felt as Little Turtle did. The Shawnees, Cherokees, Wyandots, Delawares, Potawatomis, Miamis were all hot to strike. They went to Kentucky for a showdown. The invasion did not surprise settlers, nor did it have a lasting success. The savages won a battle at Blue Licks. As soon as they retreated, George Rogers Clark with an army plunged through southern Ohio burning corn and villages.

On and off, back and forth, the struggle between white and red men kept on. First one side would score a victory, then the other. In between times the Indians raided outlying cabins.

But Little Turtle began to fear that the settlers would never be exterminated. Frontiersmen thrived like gnats and mosquitoes. Whenever some were destroyed, others swarmed in. Not even the "Year of Blood" drove out the stubborn Kentuckians.

Chapter VIII

LITTLE TURTLE TAKES A PRISONER

Little Turtle and half a dozen men moved fast over the Kentucky trail toward the Ohio River. They shaded their eyes from the glaring sun, low in the west. If they hurried they might make the river in time to cross under darkness that night. It wasn't smart to tarry too long in a land infested with settlers.

Little Turtle noticed sadly how much the landscape was beginning to change. So many holes had been cut out of the wilderness you couldn't go far without running into a clearing. In fact, there seemed to be one a little to their right. They would pass around the northwest corner of it. Little Turtle didn't remember seeing this settlement before—a cluster of six or seven cabins. Too many for a small war party to take on. It was best to swing wide and by-pass it.

"Listen!" A brave in the lead halted. "Someone is coming toward us." The men scurried into the underbrush bordering the trail and waited, guns poised. How many were coming? At least two, maybe three. Dried leaves crackled under approaching feet. The warriors fixed their eyes on the spot where the enemy would appear.

Into view came a boy, about twelve. Close behind him on the end of a rope shuffled a cow ready for the evening milking. That was all—a boy and his cow.

The boy's hair was the first thing that caught Little Turtle's eye. Never had he seen such hair! It was as orange as the streak of sun left in the sky. Little Turtle smiled.

Without warning, an Indian sprang from his hiding place and blocked the boy's path. The boy was so startled, he didn't even run. Instinctively, he lunged at the savage and belted him hard in the stomach. The Indian was completely taken off guard. He stumbled backward, tripped over a tree root and met the ground with a thud.

The boy fell on top of him. For a split second he pinned the warrior to the ground. The warrior shrieked and with a swift twist of his body, shook off the boy. But not before his comrades had witnessed the scene. Little Turtle thought it hilarious to see his powerful friend felled by a boy. He did not contain his laughter.

The warrior did not like being ridiculed. He scrambled to his feet and glowered at the boy, sprawled on the ground. With a flick of his wrist the warrior swung his tomahawk high. The club plunged toward the boy's head.

Like a fish, the boy flipped over on his belly. The

tomahawk bit the ground an inch from his ear. The warrior, off balance, was dragged to his knees by the force of the blow.

The boy wasted no time getting up. He tried to run, but Little Turtle stepped forward and gripped his shoulders from behind. By this time, the boy's angry opponent had picked himself up. He rushed forward for another attack, determined to kill the boy this time. The boy, in the iron grip of Little Turtle could not move.

"Do not kill him," commanded Little Turtle coldly. "We shall take him back to the village." The warrior let the weapon drop limp at his side. He had to obey his war chief. Still, he scowled at the boy who had made a fool of him.

Little Turtle turned to the boy and asked in broken English he had picked up from fur traders, "What is your name?"

"William. William Wells," the boy stuttered. "Everyone calls me Will."

"From now on you will be called Apakonit—wild carrot in your language," replied Little Turtle. Little Turtle could tell by the bewildered look on the boy's face that he did not understand. For a moment Little Turtle studied the boy's chest that wasn't very broad, the dirt smudges on his face and the funny red hair. There was a lot of courage packed in this boy. How Little Turtle wished he had a son like that.

He turned abruptly to his men, "Come, let us hurry to the river."

During the long journey through the wilderness, Little Turtle didn't talk to Will again. He kept him between two warriors so he couldn't escape.

It was late at night when they arrived at Little Turtle's village. But the whole village woke up. Squaws and children ran to make a fuss over the prisoner. They wanted to feel his strange red hair. A toothless squaw leered into his face and ran her shriveled hands through his hair. Will shivered. His whole body was rigid with fear.

Little Turtle sensed his fear and took him to his wigwam. Little Turtle brought out a bear skin and motioned for Will to lie down on it. Everyone else lay down, too. In a few minutes, Little Turtle was asleep.

Will drew the fur around him. Sleep was far from his mind. He knew he must get back home to Kentucky. But it was so far. Where was he? He didn't even know that. Regardless, he knew this was no time to worry about that. He must get out of the village—into the forest—as soon as possible.

He was like an animal driven by instinct, like an animal caught in a trap. He had seen how animals had gnawed off their own legs to escape a trap. He felt like that right now. He would do anything to escape.

Naturally, he had been placed farthest from the door to prevent his escape. To his left was Little Turtle. To his right were his wife and the children, so on around the circle. He would have to crawl around the fire and over one of the children. Could he make it without waking anyone?

Outside everything had quieted down. The only noise came from animals crying to each other in the night. Will strained to hear the breathing in the wigwam. It seemed steady and even. He judged that everyone was asleep.

He unwound from the bear skin, a little at a time. He rolled it back up to look as if he were still in it. He raised to his hands and knees. Now for the first step. With great effort he slid his right hand a few inches over the dirt floor. Then his left hand, then his left knee. When his right knee came forward the joint cracked. Will held his breath. He was sure it woke the whole village. He waited but no one stirred.

Carefully, he crawled between the pile of coals and Little Turtle's wife. He passed so close he could smell the sweet grease she put on her hair.

Ahead was the worst barrier—the girl's sleeping body that lay between him and the door. He hesitated a moment to make sure everyone was still breathing heavily.

He stood up, his arms dangling in front. He extended his right leg over the sleeping body. His toe touched the other side. He cautiously drew over the other leg.

The door was only a few feet. He dropped softly on all fours and crept to the door. He gingerly lifted the flap and peered out. There was no guard. The village was bare.

Sinking to his belly, he stuck his whole head under the flap. A gush of cold air washed his face and lungs. It would be only a short dash around the wigwam and into the safety of the forest.

Like a snake, he wriggled forward. His arms were out, then the top half of his body. He lay for a moment, gasping, half hysterical with joy. His heart beat like loud drums only he could hear.

Then the drums died. With horror Will felt an iron hand closing about his ankle. It was as if a steel trap had snapped on his foot. His whole body strained for a second, then went limp. He could feel himself being pulled back slowly into the wigwam. Once inside, he raised his chin off the floor. Little Turtle was squatting beside him.

"You must not try to escape, my wild carrot," said Little Turtle looking fondly on Will. "Tomorrow you become my son." Will did not comprehend and Little Turtle knew it.

Exhausted, Will lay back down on the skin. Little Turtle gently folded it over him.

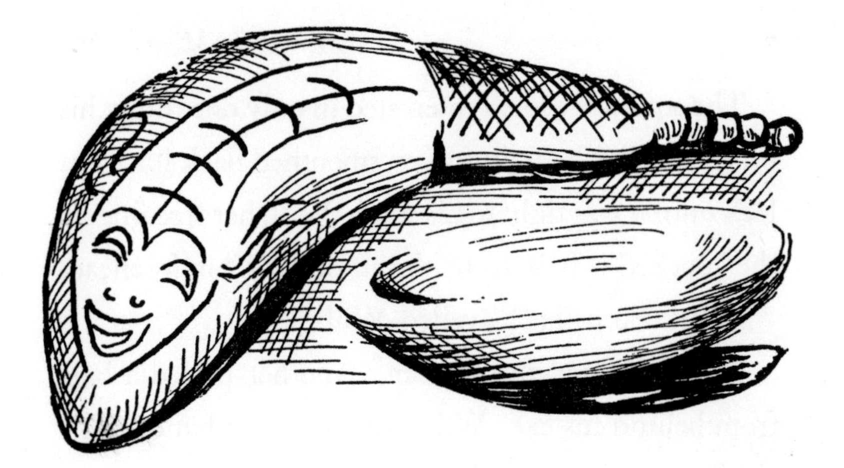

Chapter IX

SON OF A FAMOUS WAR CHIEF

The minute Will awoke he sensed it was a special day. A lot of jumbled talk was coming in through the open doorway. Everyone had left the wigwam. He lay for a moment wondering what his fate would be.

He didn't wait long. Two big squaws burst in and dragged him from the warm bear skin. They took him to another wigwam and pushed him down cross-legged onto the floor. Two more squaws appeared. One was so grotesque she reminded Will of a witch.

The squaws seemed interested in only one thing, his bright hair. The ugly squaw smoothed back his front lock until it was tight to his skull. With her free fingers she plucked a hair from the middle of his forehead.

"Ow! Stop that!" yelled Will.

This delighted the women. Another pulled a hair from behind his ear. Will swatted at her hand. This set the squaws to tittering. Then the witch-squaw decided they had had enough fun. It was time for serious business. She tied Will's hands. All four squaws settled down around him and pulled out his hairs, one by one. Occasionally, they dipped their fingers in sand to keep them from sliding off the strands of hair.

Will couldn't imagine why they wanted his hair, but he thought he must be bald by now. He learned later he was pretty close to it. The squaws left only a spot three or four inches square on top. They divided this into three locks and bound two of them with a narrow beaded garter. The other they braided and stuck full of silver brooches.

Next, two squaws gripped Will's head, another held his feet and the ugly one produced a sharp bone needle. She ran the needle through his ear lobes and the tip of his nose. Will squirmed with pain.

Then things happened rapidly. They filled his ears with earrings and nose with jewels. They took away his clothes and gave him a breach clout. They splattered paints over his body. They hung a large wampum belt over his neck. As a final touch they wound silver bands on his hands and right arm.

Smiling, they stood back and examined him. They were quite pleased with their work. Will was quite uncomfortable. One squaw fetched Little Turtle. He approved heartily of Will's appearance and led him into the street.

Little Turtle shouted and the tribe came running. Little Turtle made a long speech. Then Little Turtle motioned to three squaws who came forward and took Will down to Devil's Lake. The crowd, in high spirits, followed.

The squaws dragged Will into the water. They scrubbed and scrubbed him, but didn't harm him. Just as he took a deep breath of relief, one squaw pushed his head under water. "They are trying to drown me!" thought Will. He kicked the squaw and came up sputtering. To his astonishment, he saw a white boy on shore, shouting to him, "Don't be afraid. They are only washing away your white blood." Will relaxed a little.

The squaws escorted Will from the water to the council house. They dressed him in a ruffled shirt, a pair of leggings with ribbons and beads and moccasins. They tied a bunch of red feathers in one of his locks. Then, they presented him to Little Turtle. The chief looked deep into Will's eyes and handed him a hunting knife. Will blushed and thanked him.

The ceremony had ended. Outside a feast was beginning.

Will slipped away to find the mysterious white boy he had seen at the lake.

"What have they done to me?" asked Will.

"You are now the adopted son of Chief Little Turtle," the boy replied pleasantly. "I, too, am the adopted son of a warrior."

Will was at once relieved and despondent.

"Don't feel bad," comforted the boy. "Little Turtle is a famous war chief and will treat you well."

"I don't want to be the son of any Indian, even a chief. I want to get back to my own family," complained Will.

"That is impossible. They keep a close watch on you."

Will knew the boy was right.

Little Turtle interrupted their conversation. He spoke in the Miami language to Will's companion. "Tell Apakonit I am very proud to have him for a son. He is very much like an Indian. And that is the highest compliment I can pay a white man." The boy translated the words for Will.

Little Turtle felt that his new son was not listening.

Little Turtle spoke sternly, "Tell Apakonit, my son, not to think about escape. He is now a Miami and my son. I will treat him kindly."

Will was amazed. The chief had been able to read his mind. Little Turtle looked long into Will's eyes. An understanding passed between them. Will was confused. "I am still white, and a white man hates an Indian worse than he hates a rattler. But I don't hate this chief. I wonder why."

Little Turtle, also, was amazed by his own sudden affection for this white boy.

Chapter X

ANGRY CHIEFS

One warm day in May 1788, Little Turtle stuck his head from his wigwam and called excitedly to his white son. "Come here quickly. There is bad news you must hear."

Will hustled into the wigwam but stopped short when he saw that Little Turtle had a white visitor. Will was now eighteen and had long ago given up the idea of escaping back to Kentucky. He admired his Indian father and felt he was really his Indian son.

The thought that he was white cropped up sometimes, but he hastily buried it deep in his mind.

In an instant, Will saw that Little Turtle was unusually disturbed. Little Turtle introduced his guest. "This is Alexander McKee, a British agent. He has come straight from Fort Detroit."

Will and McKee greeted each other. Will often had heard of this fellow, and right away he didn't like him. He didn't think you could trust any of the fast-talking British. They weren't interested in the Indian's problems. All they cared about were the rich furs brought to them. In order to keep a tight grip on their fur trade, the English wanted to keep the Americans off Indian land as much as the Indians did. They were always carrying tales to inflame the Indians against the Americans.

Will glanced suspiciously at McKee and wondered what the message was this time. He judged from Little Turtle's blazing eyes that it was something alarming.

"McKee says that the Long-Knives have founded a settlement on this side of the Ohio River," said Little Turtle calmly. "On our land," Little Turtle spoke the words slowly, letting them sink in. "Do you know what that means?"

Will knew all too well. He and Little Turtle had discussed it many times. It was what the Indians feared most. It was proof that the Americans were not content below the river. They wanted to live on the northern side too, on Miami land.

McKee stroked his graying mustache. "It is just as we have been telling you all along. These Americans are moving across your land, fast. Nothing will satisfy them. They won't stop until they have pushed you onto the great plains that lie west. That is unless you stop them," he added significantly.

Will had a dozen questions about the new settlement. The only question he managed to ask was, "Is there anything to do?"

McKee began to talk, but Little Turtle cut him off.

"Yes, go now to Blue Jacket, Buckongahelas, Pecanne and LeGris. Tell them to meet me in Kekionga. Tell them I have grim news." Little Turtle's eyes snapped, and he drew himself up to full height.

Will left immediately. Little Turtle's gaze met that of McKee. Little Turtle did not like this man either. But McKee smiled a self-satisfied smile. He was delighted that the new settlement had so impressed Little Turtle. He knew Little Turtle was not easily impressed.

As history later proved, Little Turtle had good cause to be upset. That settlement, made on April 7, 1788, was at Marietta, Ohio, the first permanent settlement in the Northwest Territory. It was the opening of the whole Ohio, Indiana country. Now, it appears as a date in a history book. Then, it set the Indian world in a turmoil.

Within a few days Little Turtle and the other chiefs were sitting in the long council house at Kekionga.

Around the fire were Blue Jacket, a fiery leader of the Shawnees, and Buckongahelas, powerful chief of the Delawares. Also present were Will and McKee and Pecanne and LeGris, elder chiefs of the Miamis and still heads of the nation. But it was easy to see that only one man was in charge there. The force of Little Turtle's personality weighed heavily on everyone.

Little Turtle quickly told them of the new settlement at Marietta, but didn't wait for their reactions. He kept on, smoothly and steadily. He thought carefully, but never gave anyone time to interrupt.

"My brothers, we have all seen the white man trod over our land like a slow-moving buffalo. And we have not tried to stop him. Oh, yes, you will say we have tried with our many war parties. But these are only pricks in his skin that enrage him and drive him forward. They have done no good.

"My brothers, we have lost Kentucky, our hunting paradise where all tribes could hunt without fear. It is now a lost land. Wait—do not interrupt me, Blue

Jacket," said Little Turtle as he raised his hand.

"Even though it pains us all, we must admit Kentucky is gone forever. Pecanne, LeGris, you know none of us will ever hunt there again."

Pecanne and LeGris stared motionless at the dirt floor.

"Now the buffalo thrusts his shaggy head right into our wigwams. Are we to give up our homes, too? No, we must do something we have never done before. We must stand firm against this beast that would trample us. We must draw a line and tell him not to cross it. And that line must be the Ohio River."

McKee stroked his mustache and nodded his head. So did the others.

Little Turtle paused and Buckongahelas spoke: "But, already some of the foolish tribes have signed treaties giving away their land north of the Ohio. What can we do about that?"

"We shall do nothing," replied Little Turtle. "Those tribes were the Wyandots, Ojibways, and Ottawas.

They didn't even own the land they sold. It belonged to the Shawnees. When the white men come to claim the land, we shall not let them remain."

Little Turtle continued in earnest, "But most important, we must have all the tribes with us. You know that one man is too weak to fight a buffalo. It takes many men. Just so, it takes many tribes, all thinking as one nation, to keep the white men off our land. The tribes must lay aside all their squabbles and act as one nation to defend our land."

So that was it, thought LeGris. Little Turtle was calling for a strong confederation of tribes. The idea was certainly not new. The Miamis had always insisted on unity among tribes. LeGris did not doubt that most of the tribes would go along. And for all he knew, the confederacy might work.

The first to support Little Turtle was Blue Jacket.

"My brother," he said, "tomorrow I shall start my travels from village to village persuading the chiefs to join us. We shall build such an army that the white man will shrink with fear. You shall see, Kentucky is not lost. We shall drive them out, back across the mountains, and into the ocean."

Little Turtle replied dryly, "But first, brother, let us scare them back across the Ohio River." LeGris smiled wisely.

Little Turtle liked Blue Jacket. He was a fine warrior, a born fighter. But he was hasty, hot-headed and full of uncontrollable hate. He was a war chief without wits, who fought with sheer force, not cunning. Little Turtle felt that sooner or later he might have trouble with him. For the moment he had him under control.

Blue Jacket was not offended by Little Turtle's rebuff. He sat down. The thirst for blood still showed in his eyes.

"Buckongahelas, are you with us?" asked Little Turtle.

"Of course, my brother. I too shall start tomorrow to gather forces. It is the only thing to do."

Pecanne and LeGris agreed but declined to do any traveling. They left that to younger chiefs.

Little Turtle gave last minute instructions: "This is what you must tell other tribes. No tribe is to sign away any land to the whites. The land belongs to all Indians, not just to one tribe. Everyone is to supply warriors immediately if they are needed. Everyone must insist that the Ohio River is the boundary of the Indian nation and that no settlers shall live above it."

McKee added, "And remember, we English are behind you." McKee couldn't have been happier with the results of the council. He credited himself with arousing the Indians. He was not smart enough to sense that Little Turtle needed no urging, no British influence.

Little Turtle was independent. He was no tool of the British. He did only what he thought best for his people. If the British were willing to supply arms and ammunition he would certainly take them. But they would never tell Little Turtle what to do.

The next morning Little Turtle, Blue Jacket and Buckongahelas set off in different directions to enlist support for the confederacy. As was expected, other chiefs were quick to follow the sound leadership of the Miamis. With every passing day the confederacy gained new members and new strength. It seemed that all the tribes in the Ohio, Indiana country were massing above the Ohio River.

Little Turtle had made a bold stand for everyone to see. He had persuaded all his kinsfolk to turn a hostile face toward the white nation. It was a fierce warning to any pioneer who was planning to settle north of the Ohio.

Could Little Turtle hold off the thundering onrush of pioneers? Little Turtle didn't know, but he was sure the red men and the white were locked in a bitter struggle. Defiantly, he sat back and waited to see what would happen.

Chapter XI

NO CHANCE FOR PEACE

News of Little Turtle's confederacy swiftly reached the ears of the Americans.

A scout relayed the information to General Arthur St. Clair, new Governor of the Northwest Territory. The Northwest Territory had been created by the Northwest Ordinance, passed in 1787. As soon as possible after that St. Clair had set up governmental shop in Marietta.

Little Turtle had correctly estimated the importance

of Marietta. It was the first sure sign that the American government was spreading its wings westward.

The Northwest Ordinance also stated that the Indians should be legally paid for their land by treaty. George Washington and other leaders of the young nation felt that the Indians had been mistreated. When it came right down to it the founders of the country felt that the white man had stolen the Indian's land as if he had a right to it.

The stealing would have to stop, decided Washington. When he became president in 1789 his one policy for westward expansion was, "By all means, move west. But first, make treaties with the Indians."

In the meantime, the impact of Little Turtle's scheme was not immediately felt. Some of the Indians weakened and signed away land. As a result, Cincinnati was founded in December, 1788. During the next year more than 20,000 eager settlers floated down the Ohio River destined for the new land.

Little Turtle's warriors faithfully kept their threat

to the white invaders. Daily they hammered away at the foreigners on the river and on the Wilderness Trail.

At one place on the Ohio River, Indians sat atop a huge rock and watched the approach of a boat for miles. Sometimes they would lure the settlers to shore by forcing a white prisoner to run up and down the bank yelling for help.

These relentless attacks began to cause trouble for the government.

"We deserve protection," thousands of pioneers wailed. "Under the Northwest Ordinance, we are living on American soil."

Petitions besieged President Washington. Pressure was put on Governor St. Clair and General Harmar, commander of Fort Washington at Cincinnati. Both were old soldiers of the Revolution.

Finally General Harmar made an urgent trip to Marietta to confer with St. Clair.

"The only way to stop these savage attacks is to take an army to Kekionga," urged Harmar.

"That's out of the question." St. Clair took a piece of paper from his desk drawer. "I have orders here from President Washington that we are not to do anything so rash except as a last resort."

"Rash? But these Indians are murdering our women and children."

"Still, President Washington feels that the Indians should not be taken by force, but by treaties, Harmar, treaties!" St. Clair smiled.

"But they won't make treaties any more. This war chief Little Turtle has them all under his control. He has set the Ohio River as the frontier boundary and refuses to budge. You can't get any tribes to even talk about treaties. What does the President propose to do about this?"

"Let me read what the President says about the 'children of the forest' as he calls them. He writes: 'A due regard should be extended to those Indian tribes whose happiness so materially depends upon the national justice and humanity of the United States.' "

"Rather a soft policy, isn't it?" Harmar sneered. "But then I suppose it doesn't matter to him. He's safe far away in Philadelphia. But, over 1500 people have been killed here in the last few years."

"My dear man, I'm sure the President is aware of this. He has traveled all through this wilderness, once on horseback and once down the Ohio. He knows the situation."

"Then why no army?" countered Harmar.

"The main reason is the President feels that the Indians will eventually back down when they see we really mean to move west. He insists on an 'honorable' purchase of land from the Indians. He also believes land should be set aside for the Indians so they will not be molested."

St. Clair continued, "However, Washington reports that Secretary of War Henry Knox has some other very good arguments against all-out war. In the first place the people back East are against it. They don't think much of a pioneer. They have heard so many stories of murders on both sides that they figure the white men are just as guilty as the Indians.

"Secondly, we can get neither money nor men to carry on an invasion. There are approximately 600 soldiers scattered out here. The Secretary estimates we would need at least 1900 men. The whole thing would cost about $200,000. The Secretary says that's out of the question.

"Another thing. Government officials are sure we can arrange peace without expense and without bloodshed."

"Just what do we do next?" inquired Harmar.

"Washington suggests that we send a messenger of peace through the villages immediately. Do you know of someone who would go?"

Harmar thought. "Yes, I have the man. But I can tell you right now it won't do any good. The only thing Little Turtle understands is an army, the bigger the better. But, we'll try once more. Then maybe the government will agree with me."

"Perhaps you are right. I can't entirely disagree, but we must carry out orders. Send the messenger as soon as possible."

General Harmar did just that as soon as he returned to Fort Washington. He chose an intelligent French merchant, named Antoine Gamelin. He thought a Frenchman would be more successful than an American because the Indians had always been friendly with the French.

Gamelin's mission was to persuade the suspicious Indians that the Americans wanted to live in peace, side by side with their Indian brothers. He was to bring back an answer from the tribes.

Gamelin set out in the spring of 1790. The first village he visited was cordial but evasive. Little Turtle had taught them well. Their answer was: "We cannot say anything until we consult the Miamis."

The situation at the village of the Piankeshaws was the same. They would have to consult their eldest brothers, the Miamis. At every village the answer was the same. They told Gamelin to go to Kekionga and bring back a report from Little Turtle.

Deeper in Indian country Gamelin ran into open hostility, first at a Kickapoo village then at Ouiatenon on the Wabash River. Undiscouraged, he finally reached Kekionga only to find Little Turtle absent.

Still, he called together the Miamis, Shawnees and Delawares and gave them peace tokens of wampum. Chiefs LeGris and Buckongehelas seemed friendly, but would make no decision.

Blue Jacket didn't conceal his bitter hatred of Gamelin and all white men. He said he would trust the Long-Knives as he trusted a copperhead ready to strike. He said that if the Americans were so sincere, why did they build new settlements in Marietta and Cincinnati.

Gamelin left with only a slight satisfaction. The Miamis said they would send an answer within thirty days to Fort Vincennes. Gamelin doubted that any answer would come and if it did he was pretty sure it would be "No." He didn't have to wait that long. Before he ever reached the fort, the Indians sent their answer. They hit the warpath again.

After the peace messenger had failed, General Harmar went once again to Marietta to see Governor St. Clair. This time the talk was strictly military. Even Washington and Knox agreed it was time for the last resort.

"All right, Harmar, we have the orders we have been waiting for. Both Washington and Knox say you should take an army to Kekionga, home of Chief Little Turtle."

"At last," sighed Harmar.

"But," warned St. Clair, "President Washington wants to make clear that this is not a war of revenge against the Indians. It is only a means to subdue the warriors a little. Just enough so the settlers can forge ahead. In other words, knock down this frontier barrier Little Turtle has set up."

"But, don't rout the Indians. Is that right?"

"Yes, and be careful. Secretary Knox is worried about the results. He doesn't want to start a full-scale war over this patch of wilderness that might involve England again. And one more thing, you are not to establish a fort at Kekionga. Just burn the wigwams and food supplies."

"When do I start?" asked Harmar eagerly.

"That depends on how soon you can raise the men. Of course, you know you don't have a lot of government support for the campaign. The men you're able to scrounge up may be pretty ragged."

"Ragged or not. They don't have to be the best troops to beat savages."

"Well, anyway, good luck to you. And remember, not too much bloodshed."

"All right. I won't give them a real whipping. Just enough to frighten them."

Chapter XII

TRICKED!

General Josiah Harmar stood erect in his crisp blue uniform and three-cornered hat. It was September 30, 1790. He hastily surveyed the troops that were lined up, ready for the march to Kekionga. Then he turned crossly to one of his officers: "This is hardly my idea of a United States Army."

Harmar recalled that St. Clair had said the troops might be poor. But never had Harmar imagined that they might be this bad.

Part of them were feeble old men with matted gray hair and beards. They leaned on their muskets as if they were canes. Harmar doubted that many would be able to hobble to the fort gate, let alone the rough 150 miles to Kekionga.

In contrast, many others were boys with faces as smooth as plums. They joked about how good they looked in their new uniforms. Harmar knew that most of the boys had never been away from home until now.

Everything seemed to go wrong from the beginning. Pennsylvania hadn't supplied as many troops as she had promised. The government hadn't sent enough camp kettles and axes. Most of the Kentucky militia showed up with muskets that needed repairing. Harmar declared that they had scraped up all the broken muskets in the Kentucky area.

The only bright spot in the army was 320 trained, experienced troops from the regular army. In these Harmar placed his hopes. Regardless, he was convinced that it wouldn't take much to beat an unorganized bunch of redskins.

Harmar bit his lip and gave a brave command to march. The doors of Fort Washington swung wide and 1,153 men in blue filed out. Destination: Kekionga. The first United States Army of the Indian Wars was on its way. With it went the hopes of all settlers from Marietta to Louisville.

The army cut straight north, following the west side of what is now Ohio. It crossed the Little Miami River and Glade Creek on the present side of Xenia, Ohio. Then it set a northwest course. It crossed the stream above the present site of Piqua, Ohio and the St. Marys River.

Chief Little Turtle's curious eyes were ever on the slow-moving army. He knew right where they were every minute. His swift-footed scouts watched from behind trees and peered from hilltops. Then they raced to Kekionga with reports of the enemy position.

Little Turtle watched the soldiers press farther into

sacred Miami country. He did not molest them. In fact, Little Turtle was so calm that his warriors became nervous. They wondered if he was going to sit still and let the soldiers take Kekionga.

Blue Jacket was in a panic. He urged Little Turtle to lead warriors to meet the advancing army.

Little Turtle smiled. He whispered his secret war plan to Blue Jacket. "Do you agree?" Little Turtle demanded. Blue Jacket's mouth sagged in open admiration.

Other chiefs were equally impressed by Little Turtle's plan. All Little Turtle had to do now was watch and wait like a wildcat in a tree.

When the American army reached the St. Marys River, General Harmar made an important decision. He sent 600 militia under Colonel John Hardin to conquer Kekionga.

When Little Turtle learned this, he issued strict orders: "Bury all the corn you can. Burn the rest. Burn all wigwams. We shall not provide food for the enemy.

Then run! Run for your lives along the trail to the northwest."

"But, Father," Will objected, "the white soldiers will easily be able to follow the trail over which we have fled."

"Yes, they will, won't they?" smiled Little Turtle.

Colonel Hardin and his men found Kekionga deserted and dotted by piles of ashes. Colonel Hardin turned his men loose. For three days they destroyed everything within sight. They butchered several cows that were wandering in a meadow. They discovered and burned over 20,000 bushels of corn the Indians had hidden.

Hardin let his men roam without orders while he reported to General Harmar. The general was now camped at the junction of the St. Joseph and Maumee rivers.

Colonel Hardin felt cheated. "We came all this way for nothing. They have all fled like scared rabbits."

"Calm down, Colonel," replied General Harmar. "We have come for a fight and we shall find one. We have discovered the tracks of squaws and children leading northwest out of the village. Obviously, they ran so fast they didn't have time to cover their escape."

"We know they won't come out in a face to face fight with us. We'll have to search them out, track them down, and force them to fight," stormed Hardin.

"Exactly what I was thinking," said Harmar. "I'm sending you and your men on ahead over that Indian trail. Find them and bring them to battle."

Hardin rallied his men and eagerly set out on the trail. The brown earth was notched with hundreds of moccasin prints.

Five or six miles outside Kekionga the soldiers found an abandoned Indian camp. Hardin was like a bloodhound on the trail. He plunged ahead, carelessly, without scouts.

Suddenly the path bulged into a narrow prairie bordered by heavy timber. Hardin spotted a campfire and scattered Indian trinkets at the far end of the prairie. "We're hot on their heels, men! Forward!" he boomed.

From his hiding place in the underbrush, Little Turtle watched the soldiers pour into the small open prairie. As soon as they were neatly packed in, he took a deep breath and threw back his powerful head. A sharp war cry quivered on the air then died. Three hundred Miami warriors opened fire.

The American soldiers were confused. Dozens slumped to the ground. Nearly all the others dropped their guns and dashed headlong for the trail over which they had come.

"Retreat. Run for your lives!" they screamed. They trampled each other squeezing through the narrow bottleneck to the trail. Colonel Hardin was one of the first to reach safety. Only the regular soldiers stayed to fight. Little Turtle's forces soon killed all except five or six who escaped.

The whole battle lasted but fifteen minutes.

Little Turtle emerged from his hiding place, as a cloud of smoke settled over the blue-coated dead.

The last of the soldiers were racing back along the trail. They turned and fired a couple of times. Warriors started to chase them, but Little Turtle called the warriors back. "It is enough." He waved his hand over the dead soldiers. "We shall have other times."

In a moment, Will was at Little Turtle's side. The gaze of the two men met. Will's eyes were full of wild excitement.

"You were right," Will grinned brightly, "they were able to follow the trail quite easily." Little Turtle did not answer.

Will glanced uneasily down at a blood-spattered soldier, lying near his feet. His eyes traveled up over the crumpled uniform to the face, dug in the dirt. It was a boy and his face was white—white as a sycamore. Will felt his own face. He knew it was white, too. Now it was damp and cold. He turned away, about to be sick.

Little Turtle did not notice. He was in a world of his own. He looked wonderingly into the dark trees that separated him from Kekionga and the white army. He had clearly outwitted them this time. But would they flee back to Fort Washington? Or would they be angry enough to try an attack? Only time would tell.

Chapter XIII

A RIVER OF BLOOD

General Harmar was enraged over Colonel Hardin's shameful defeat. The general snorted at Hardin, "It is not enough that we let Little Turtle outwit us. The cowardice of the militia was outrageous. They threw down their guns and ran. They hardly fired a shot!"

Colonel Hardin's hasty excuses seemed very flimsy to Harmar. He would not hear them. "I'm ordering an about face. We're heading back to Fort Washington immediately!"

The army retreated seven miles southeast of Kekionga and camped. Colonel Hardin's pride was smarting from the disgraceful defeat. He gathered courage and went to General Harmar's tent. Colonel Hardin begged the general, "Let me take a force back to Kekionga now."

"What good would that do?" Harmar objected.

"By this time the savages have returned to Kekionga. We could easily surprise them."

General Harmar turned the idea over in his mind. The men had tramped so far through swamps and forest. The expedition was costing the government several thousand dollars. They couldn't return defeated. The prestige of the general and the federal government would sink. Harmar knew he must take any chance to beat the savages and save face.

"All right, Colonel Hardin, take about 350 militia plus 50 or 60 of our best regulars."

Late that night the soldiers slipped out of camp. At sunup, advance scouts mounted a hill overlooking Kekionga. Several Indians were on their hands and knees digging for buried corn. Others were searching for their belongings in smoking embers. A natural quiet sat on the village. Colonel Hardin was sure the Indians did not for an instant suspect an attack.

Colonel Hardin revealed his battle plans to his officers. One battalion was to swing across the St. Marys River and came in on the west of Kekionga. The others were to ford the Maumee and close in from the south, east and north. Thus, the Indians would be surrounded and unable to escape the crossfire. Colonel Hardin's plan seemed fool-proof. But he didn't count on the shrewdness of his opponent, Chief Little Turtle.

Not for one moment after his victory had Little Turtle lowered his guard. He had kept hawk's eyes on the enemy. He knew the soldiers were moving back toward Kekionga. His scouts had awakened him in the night to inform him.

After Little Turtle had dismissed the scouts he squatted silently in his dark wigwam. He needed an unusual battle plan. It would not be easy to take on 400 soldiers, some of them crack troops from the regular army.

He searched his memory for war tricks. He recreated battle scenes. He recalled all the war lessons he had learned as a boy. Then something his father had told him many years ago stuck in his mind. "Try to read the enemy's mind."

It made sense. Little Turtle recalled that during yesterday's battle, four militia officers had deserted to chase a lone Indian.

A bold plan was churning in Little Turtle's sharp mind. If four soldiers would pursue one Indian, wouldn't many soldiers pursue eight or ten Indians? With Indian decoys, Little Turtle might be able to lure the advance guard away from the regular soldiers. Then the regulars would be exposed to brutal attack. Little Turtle knew it was a daring stab. Its success would depend on how well he could read the enemy's mind.

In the morning Little Turtle concealed his men at the northern bank of the Maumee where the soldiers were to cross. First came the militia splashing through the water. Then the regulars. As soon as the militia emerged on dry land, Little Turtle ordered a dozen Indians to jump up and flee. This was the crucial moment. Would the militia give chase? Little Turtle's heart stopped beating.

"Hey, there they go!" screeched a horseman and galloped off to the right. Others were close behind.

Now the body of regulars was alone in the river without the advance guard. The blue-clad men struggled forward, holding guns high above their heads. A few climbed up on the bank.

They were so close Little Turtle could see their faces. Still he did not shoot. He had ordered his men to hold their fire until the soldiers were on top of them.

As a soldier crashed through the underbrush, Little Turtle signaled. His warriors fired.

Men toppled off the bank into the water. Dozens

slumped into the water. Little Turtle had caught them in the open with no cover. Soldiers stumbled toward the opposite bank. Only a handful made it. One-hundred and eighty-three sank into watery graves. Their bodies formed a bridge from shore to shore.

Colonel Hardin heard the fighting. He was horrified that his plan was ruined. He galloped to General Harmar and sought fresh troops. The general blanched. "Great heavens, man! Do you think I'm mad! I'm not sending any more men to be butchered."

Harmar packed up and hurried his men back to Fort Washington. The return trip was dismal. But the reception at Fort Washington was even worse. Once hopeful faces of settlers darkened. Soon the word of the campaign's failure was all over the frontier.

The whole nation was shocked.

General Harmar had to admit that not once, but twice, he had been outwitted by a clever Indian war chief.

"But what savage could have conceived such brilliant tactics?" asked the worried Governor St. Clair.

"I know of only one," murmured General Harmar. "Chief Little Turtle of the Miamis."

Chapter XIV

"GENERAL, BEWARE A SURPRISE!"

After the defeat of Harmar's army everyone was in an uproar—the Indians, pioneers, and government. The cause of it all was Little Turtle.

To the pioneers he was a terrible curse. They shuddered when his name was mentioned. To government officials he was a nuisance that had to be disposed of so the country could expand its borders.

But to his own people, Little Turtle was a hero. He made the self-confidence of his people soar. He was the symbol of a fierce hope that the red nation had not known before. For years the Indian nation had been steadily weakening. It had sunk to its knees before the onrushing white conquerers. It was in grave danger of falling flat on its back and dying.

Now along had come a powerful war chief who sent the white army scurrying back behind safe walls at Fort Washington. It was a sign of new life, new strength. Little Turtle was a strong heart, pumping new life blood through his feeble nation.

The pulse of the Indian nation quickened and grew stronger. It echoed in the furious pounding of the war drums. It echoed in the patter of soft moccasins on trails to white settlements.

Following Harmar's defeat, all Indians hit the warpath with new determination. This time, they were going to stop the white enemies forever.

Little Turtle, too, felt that the Indian nation was getting back on its feet. But he knew it was not good to be foolhardy. He knew the Americans had not given up their conquest. "They will be back," he often told Will during that bleak winter of 1790 and 1791. "When they do, we must be ready again and we must be strong."

There was no doubt about it. The United States government would have to do something soon. Settlers had predicted that the Indians would be worse after beating Harmar's army. But not even settlers had imagined that the Indian raids would be so bold or frequent.

It was never safe to venture outside the stockade. Those who did never returned. Their bodies were discovered months later.

Also, new settlers feared to float down the Ohio River to claim the cheap lands of the frontier. Indians patrolled the waters day and night.

For four hundred miles along the Ohio River, settlers lived in terror.

Citizens of the western part of Virginia appealed to their state government. "The frontier has to be held

somewhere," they said. "Why not right where it is, after all the blood we pioneers have shed. We must never move back. That would be admitting defeat. All would be lost."

President Washington was inclined to agree. But he faced a problem. The Easterners didn't want to spend money for another Indian campaign. They had been outraged that Harmar's army had been routed by uncivilized natives. Stern Easterners said that nothing would be worth another campaign.

President Washington studied the arguments from both sides. He decided that another army must attack Kekionga. Settlement of the new nation had to proceed.

He told Congress his feelings. Finally, he persuaded the lawmakers to pass an act in March, 1791, making provisions for the protection of our frontier. After that law, the wheels of government began to move faster.

Washington appointed Governor St. Clair new commander-in-chief of the army in the northwest. This caused some surprise. St. Clair had been a Revolutionary War officer. Now he was fifty-seven and often so sick with gout he could hardly mount his horse. He had had no experience fighting Indians. And the long hard trudge through Indian country was not easy, even for a young, experienced leader.

Nevertheless, Washington had confidence in St. Clair. St. Clair went to Philadelphia to discuss his orders with Washington and Secretary of War Knox.

The Secretary said, "You are to commence a march to the Miami Village (Kekionga) and establish a strong permanent military post there. During your advance you shall establish such posts of communication with Fort Washington as you judge proper."

"How many men will I have?" asked St. Clair.

"We have authorized you to raise a force of 3,000 men for the campaign. That should be more than enough."

St. Clair nodded halfheartedly. He had little appetite for such a rough expedition. But he had consented because he felt that it was his duty to do so.

He turned to depart. President Washington rose from behind his heavy oak desk and wished General St. Clair good luck.

"And, one last warning," said the President forcefully, "beware of a surprise, general! Beware of a surprise!"

During the summer of 1791, men were recruited for St. Clair's expedition. They were picked up right off the street. Some were even taken out of prisons in the city. Their pay was low. Privates were given $2.10 a month; sergeants, $3.60 a month.

The soldiers were restless. They wanted to go back home. They fought among themselves. Many deserted.

It is not surprising that these men formed the most miserable army in our country's history. Harmar's army had looked bad, but St. Clair's was even worse, in spite of its larger size.

General Harmar said he was astonished that St.

Clair should think of risking his reputation and life and the lives of so many others by setting out with such an army.

Harmar thought that the Indians were superior to or equal to the best men the Americans could take against them. Little Turtle had taught Harmar respect for the Indian foe.

But St. Clair did not heed warnings. Early in September, 1791, St. Clair and 2,000 men marched forward. Although he had counted on 3,000, he was not upset. He thought he would win merely by outnumbering the Indians.

Twenty-five miles north, the army erected a new post on the eastern bank of the Great Miami. They called it Fort Hamilton. After marching forty-two miles farther, they built another garrison and named it Fort Jefferson.

After that, bad luck rode all the way with the expedition. It rained and rained. The horses faltered knee deep in mud. The supply wagons couldn't move. General St. Clair and his second in command, General Richard Butler, had an argument. The two weren't speaking. St. Clair was stricken with a bad case of gout.

Every day St. Clair's aide, Major Ebenezer Denny, carried terrible reports to St. Clair's tent.

"Sir, we don't have enough tents, pack saddles, kettles, knapsacks."

"Sir, the provisions are mouth-to-mouth now."

"Sir, the men are dying from starvation and the fever."

"Sir, the soldiers are deserting every day, sometimes as many as twenty and thirty at a time."

On October 31, Major Denny burst into St. Clair's tent with an alarming report. "General, today at least sixty of the militia have turned back. They threaten to loot our supply wagons in the rear."

St. Clair pulled himself up on his elbow. "Enough of this. We cannot tolerate any more desertions. Send Major Hamtramck to bring them back."

"But, sir, that is our best regiment. The Major is our most experienced Indian fighter. Suppose we had a surprise attack while he was gone?"

"A surprise attack, *here?* Nonsense! The Indians are still miles away, to our northwest, my boy. They won't come out of Kekionga to fight. We have to go in after them. When we get a little closer, we'll look out for a surprise attack."

Major Hamtramck and his regiment swung back to pursue the deserters.

One of Little Turtle's scouts followed the regiment for a while. Then he slapped his pony and galloped off in the direction of Kekionga.

But the Indian scout didn't have to take his report all the way to Kekionga. Little Turtle was no longer so far away. In fact, he and 1,000 warriors were camped only a few miles north of St. Clair's army.

Little Turtle calmly heard his scout's message. He said nothing. But anyone close enough could have seen a light come into his dark eyes.

He walked toward Blue Jacket and Buckongahelas who were warming themselves by the campfire. In a few seconds, the three chiefs were huddled close together, talking excitedly. The light was still in Little Turtle's eyes.

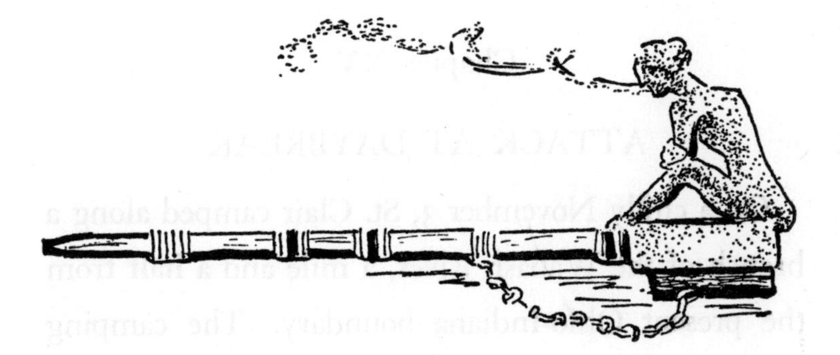

Chapter XV

ATTACK AT DAYBREAK

On a chilly November 3, St. Clair camped along a branch of the Wabash River, a mile and a half from the present Ohio-Indiana boundary. The camping ground was a pleasant meadow, circled by a dense forest. The troops were cramped in a small space. The militia were settled across the Wabash.

Before retiring that night, General St. Clair emerged from his tent for a last minute inspection of his camp. The ground was powdered with snow. The forest was full of night screams. St. Clair blew his nose loudly. He said a few chilly words to General Butler. Then both men went to their tents.

St. Clair fell asleep instantly. But General Butler couldn't sleep. He heard the outlying sentries occasionally fire at a prowling Indian. Finally he got up and ordered intelligence officers to go out and find out what was going on.

They returned with frightening reports. Indian scouts were surveying the camp. Surely, they would attack in the morning. "Shall I inform General St. Clair?" the intelligence officer asked.

"No," replied Butler. "You must get some rest."

The man looked confused and distressed, but he obeyed Butler's orders.

General St. Clair was not informed that the Indians were studying the camp. For some strange, unknown reason, General Butler kept the dreadful secret to himself. The whole camp slept peacefully as if nothing were happening around them.

At daybreak, St. Clair was awakened by an explosion of gunfire. Next he heard shouts and the sound of men running every which way. In a second, the bugles blasted their tin call to arms. St. Clair painfully lifted his foot off his bed and hobbled out of his tent.

Indians in the surrounding woods were plowing bullets into the camp from all directions. Dozens of soldiers were already sprawled on the cold ground. A vast cloud of smoke settled over the camp. Soldiers couldn't even see where to fire. Shadows of men darted here and there in the white haze. Officers shouted orders but no one paid any attention.

St. Clair moved frantically among his troops trying to restore order.

At last, the army's cannons turned their noses toward the trees. With each shot several savages collapsed. But the artillery did not last long. A group of Indian sharpshooters, led by William Wells, picked off the gunners, one by one. Finally all of them lay curled around the gun wheels. The big guns were silent.

Time and again the officers rallied charges against the Indian lines. But the Americans made no headway. Exposed in the open and unable to see, they didn't have a chance.

Within three hours, St. Clair saw that hundreds were dead. The survivors were huddled together, firing desperately into the woods. St. Clair knew they would all die if they didn't get out. In despair, he ordered a retreat. "Charge through the Indian lines!"

The soldiers burst through the Indian lines. General St. Clair was forgotten in the mad rush. He hobbled on his sore foot toward the road. Major Denny put him on the only remaining horse—a pack horse. The feeble general, atop a slow stepping pack horse, rode away from the scene of the battle.

Behind he left over 600 bodies strewn on the ground. Among them were fifty-six women who were the wives and sweethearts of the soldiers. Little Turtle lost only thirty braves. It was the greatest military disaster in American history.

When President Washington learned of the defeat he was furious with General St. Clair. "I warned him, 'Beware of a surprise.' Yet he let his army be cut to pieces by an Indian surprise—the very thing I warned him against. How can he ever answer to his country?"

St. Clair did answer to a committee of Congress. Evidently his answer was convincing. They found him blameless for the massacre. Still his career was ruined. In a short time he was removed from the office of Governor of the Northwest Territory and commander-in-chief of the Northwest army. He later died in poverty.

After St. Clair's catastrophe, the whole Northwest Territory was once again gripped with terror. The United States government seemed powerless to do anything about it. Two armies and two disgraceful defeats!

Was Chief Little Turtle going to hold off the whole United States Army forever?

Chapter XVI

STRANGE VOICES FROM THE WIND

The winter and spring after that famous battle Little Turtle heard little from the white men. No more armies had come.

Then in the summer of 1792 reports came that an army was forming at Fort Pitt (Pittsburgh, Pennsylvania). Then the army moved to Fort Washington and became bigger. In the fall of 1793 the army moved north. Now it lay camped deep in Indian country on the very site where St. Clair had met defeat.

Little Turtle was worried about this new army, but he kept his fears to himself. Then one day he told Will as the two sat under a giant elm tree.

"I talked to the British agent, Alexander McKee. He says the British will send us arms and ammunition to fight the army of the Long-Knives."

Will did not answer.

"It is not wise to fight," said Little Turtle.

Will was astounded. "Why?"

"I have watched this new army march into our land. This army is not like the two we drove out. It is led by a chief who never sleeps. Day and night he makes battle plans and drills his soldiers. During his long journey we have never once been able to surprise him. Perhaps we will not win this time."

Will had never heard Little Turtle speak this way.

"I would not talk so to anyone but you," Little Turtle mumbled sadly. "It is not right that a war chief should forsake a chance to fight." He added, "But, I am no longer a *young* war chief."

Will could see that it was so. Little Turtle was now forty-two. His black scalp lock was tinted with gray. Wrinkles were spread around his small dark eyes. Even his ears had wrinkled under the heavy silver earrings that ran down his back. Yet, his arms and legs were as hard as ever.

"You're still strong as a young man," replied Will. "You haven't aged any."

"Yes, my ideas are growing older." Little Turtle recalled that his father had once told him, the old and young think differently. Little Turtle knew now what he had meant.

Despair crept into his voice, "When I was a young man, I thought we could keep the Americans beyond the Ohio River."

"And you don't now?" asked Will.

"No, at night I lay awake and listen to the wind. It whispers to me that the Americans will never give up. It tells me that they will finally take our lands from us."

"You will not fight anymore?"

"I would fight to my death to keep my fathers' lands if it were possible. But maybe it is hopeless. And I do not want to see my people killed in a useless war."

"I am glad to hear you speak so," replied Will. "I wish peace would come between the white man and the Indian. For I have been troubled by guilt. Now I can tell you. Father, I must leave the tribe. I must go back to my own people."

Little Turtle took a deep breath. He was surprised and deeply hurt, but knew he must not show it. "When did you decide, my son?"

"Last night. I, too, listen to the wind at night. And it tells me I am a white man."

"You have been thinking about it for a long while?"

"Yes, for several years, ever since the first battle I fought against General Harmar. When I saw that the soldiers were my own people, it made me think about myself. Then after the destruction of St. Clair's army

I began to worry that some of the soldiers I killed might be my own kinsfolk from Kentucky."

"Will you go back to Kentucky?" asked Little Turtle quietly.

"No, I will go to the new army. Maybe they can use me as a scout."

Sadness came into Little Turtle's eyes. Now his white son would be fighting against him.

Will saw the look. "It pains me to leave you, but I must."

"Yes," Little Turtle's eyes softened. "You are still my son, but you are no longer an Indian. You must be my enemy now."

Will and Little Turtle stood up. Will clasped his hand. Little Turtle said, "We have long been friends. We are friends yet until the sun reaches the middle of the sky. From that time we are enemies."

Will hurried down the hill and crossed the river. Little Turtle watched until he was out of sight.

Then Little Turtle walked slowly back toward Kekionga. The wind was muttering in the trees. Little Turtle did not listen to it. He knew it was saying sad things. Things he didn't want to hear.

Chapter XVII

"IS LITTLE TURTLE AFRAID?"

"General Wayne, there's a white man out here, all dressed up like an Indian," called out a sentry. "He says he wants to see you."

Thus, William Wells was introduced to General Anthony Wayne, tough commander of the new army Little Turtle feared. At first Wayne was suspicious of Will. He thought he was an Indian spy. But Will persuaded him otherwise.

"All right, then, Wells. You're a scout. Get yourself some decent breeches and a coonskin cap. When that red hair of yours grows out, maybe you'll look like a white man again."

After a few weeks in camp, Will could see that Little Turtle had been right about Wayne's army. They were well disciplined and trained soldiers. They were not like the groups that had served under Generals Harmar and St. Clair.

Wayne was quick to tell why. "You would never know these are men I picked up off the street. I spent two long years training them. I had them drilling in the snow. I made them look like soldiers, talk like soldiers, feel like soldiers. I waited and waited until the men were ready. I wasn't going to dash headlong into a massacre the way Harmar and St. Clair did."

Wayne was a good solid officer. He was a hero of the Revolutionary War. In addition, he was an experienced Indian fighter. He was full of energy and extremely popular with his troops.

Washington had been hesitant about appointing

him. Wayne fought so fiercely that he had been nicknamed "Mad" Anthony. Washington was afraid such a man would draw the United States into a larger war than it could handle. Nevertheless, in April, 1792, Washington named Wayne commander of the northwest army.

After Wayne's appointment, the government kept up its peace offers to the Indians. All efforts failed. At last in September, 1793, Secretary of War Knox wrote to Wayne: "Every effort has been made to obtain peace. There is nothing left to expect but war."

Wayne had pulled out of Fort Washington immediately. He had erected a post above Fort Washington and called it Fort Greenville. (This is the present city of Greenville, Ohio). Here Wayne spent the winter and Will Wells joined him in the spring of 1794. Later Will became Captain of the Scouts.

Wells proved to be a valuable scout. He and another scout, named Miller, who had also been adopted by Indians, were kept busy. The two men were always galloping up in front of Wayne's house with reports.

One day in the summer Will brought big news. "At least 2,000 warriors and their families are gathering along the Maumee River above where it joins the Auglaize." Will did not mention that he had seen his Indian father, Little Turtle, walking in the lowlands. Will could tell his upright walk even from a great distance.

"What are they doing there?" asked Wayne.

"They have built bark huts and planted vegetables. Their corn must stretch for fifty miles. I would say they plan to fight there. Many of them have come from Kekionga. There are Miamis, Delawares, and all the tribes of Little Turtle's confederacy."

"Their camp must be near the British Fort Miami," said Wayne.

"That's right. I think the Indians have moved just to be close to the fort. They are counting on support from the British. Alexander McKee, British Indian agent, also has a trading post nearby. He always encourages the Indians to fight and promises them aid."

Wayne jumped up. He was not very tall, but he had a commanding appearance and voice. "I think it is time our army started moving north to meet these savages."

On July 26, Wayne's army received wagons of supplies. Two days later it left Fort Greenville and pushed into the upper Indian country. They passed through Fort Recovery which Wayne had erected the winter before. This was where St. Clair had left 600 bodies almost three years before. Some 24 miles north Wayne also garrisoned a post and called it Fort Adams.

It was a long slow march. Wayne took every protection against an Indian surprise attack. On August 8, the force reached the junction of the Maumee and the Auglaize rivers. Here was a deserted Indian village, strewn with empty wigwams. All around it were green meadows, cornfields, vegetables, and orchards. Wayne was struck by its beauty. "This is a perfect site for a fort," he decided.

So the soldiers began hacking logs for the first permanent fort deep in Indian country. It was a sure sign that the Americans meant to stay. Wayne gave it the appropriate name of Fort Defiance. It is now Defiance, Ohio.

While the fort was being constructed, Wayne sent one last peace offer to the confederate tribes gathered on the Maumee. Wayne asked their chiefs to meet him anywhere for a treaty. He warned them against trusting the British. He begged them not to shut their ears to his last offer of peace.

General Wayne had no idea what a furor that peace message would cause among the Indians.

Little Turtle, Blue Jacket and the other chiefs met in the council house. They were to decide what kind of a message to send back to the great white chief. They had no intention of taking the peace message seriously. They planned to send a reply that would stall for time so they could get more arms from the British.

Without a word, Little Turtle listened to the talk. He was torn inside. He was wrought with concern for his people's welfare. Yet he was a war chief and a war chief fought. Should he speak his mind?

Finally, he could stand it no longer. He stood up, his feet braced far apart. He looked every bit a fierce war chief. Everyone was silent to hear his words. But no one expected what came from his lips.

"My brothers, the wind whispers to me we should listen to the offers of peace."

A horrible gasp went around the circle of warriors. They were all stunned. Surely, their war chief did not mean it. A few objected.

"No, let me continue," said Little Turtle. "We have beaten the enemy twice under different commanders. We cannot expect to win always. Now the Americans are led by a chief who never sleeps. All the time he has been marching toward our villages, we have never been able to surprise him. Think well on what I say."

Little Turtle searched for the eyes of his warriors.

But their heads hung low. Their eyes were downcast. There was a hushed silence in every corner of the council house.

Suddenly, Blue Jacket jumped up, his face red with anger. "Can it be that Little Turtle is afraid of the Long-Knives? Is he afraid to fight? Is he afraid to die?"

Little Turtle's eyes blazed. Not a muscle moved in his face. "Little Turtle would gladly die if it would drive out the white men. But hundreds of our people may die in a foolish battle."

Blue Jacket did not even listen. He said slyly, "Or is it that Little Turtle does not want to fight against his white son who now rides with the Long-Knives?"

Little Turtle's eyes were hard. "Blue Jacket, you know your accusation is unjust. You are a very foolish war chief. You should want to do what is best for your people. Instead, all you think of is fighting back, as a clumsy, angry buffalo fights. You do not know, as I do, that the white men will settle on our land."

"Does the wind tell you that?" snarled Blue Jacket. "Brave warriors are not frightened by the howling wind!"

In the dim light Little Turtle looked down at the seated warriors. They were all eyes now. They followed the argument excitedly. But Little Turtle could see they were on the side of Blue Jacket.

"Are you warriors?" shouted Blue Jacket. "Yes!" they roared.

Little Turtle felt sick deep in his stomach. There was no use to speak further. The warriors had made up their minds. They were following Blue Jacket to war. This was the first time Little Turtle had ever felt powerless.

"Well, are you with us, Little Turtle?" asked Blue Jacket defiantly.

"Yes," murmured Little Turtle sadly. "If my people will not listen—if they choose to fight—the least I can do is fight side by side with them."

Outside, in the warm night, Blue Jacket slung his

arm around Little Turtle's shoulder. "Look, Little Turtle, there is no wind tonight. Not even a breeze. The night says nothing. Surely, it is a good sign."

Little Turtle stared Blue Jacket full in the eyes. "We shall soon see." Then he walked away.

Chapter XVIII

"CHARGE!"

General Wayne studied the Indians' reply to his final offer of peace. "They want us to wait ten days for their answer. That will give them ten days to round up warriors and get more arms from the British. Isn't that their trick?" The general faced his captain of the scouts, William Wells.

"Yes, sir, I'd say so."

"Well, we're not waiting here at Fort Defiance any longer. We're moving out now. We shall begin and end the Indian War once and for all," declared Wayne.

On August 17, 1794, Wayne's army pulled out of Fort Defiance and pushed to the head of the Maumee Rapids. Here they began building Fort Deposit.

On the evening of the 19th, the camp buzzed with excitement. General Wayne, at long last, issued orders for battle. "At daybreak, we shall march forth in combat formation. We shall find the enemy wherever he is hiding. And we shall conquer him!"

A harsh cheer went up from the men.

The general continued, "Don't carry packs or blankets, or anything else heavy enough to hamper your movement. All you need are guns and ammunition!"

Another shout echoed through the trees. For over two years the troops had waited for this moment. At last they were going to meet those dreaded redskins. That night the soldiers lay around the popping campfire. They talked with excitement. It was an excitement that comes from fear that they may not survive the battle. They knew they might never return to their homes in Pennsylvania, Virginia and Kentucky.

Late that night General Wayne retired to his shabby tent with Will. Wayne wore his old blue coat. He sat on the side of his bed in the dim light.

Wells sat opposite him. Will no longer looked like the son of Little Turtle. He wore the uniform of a captain in the United States Army. His bright orange hair was completely grown out.

General Wayne was not really nervous. But he was concerned. "Wells, were you able to find out where the red devils are hiding?"

"Not exactly, sir. I'd say about ten miles ahead of us, somewhere near the British fort."

"Do you think they are waiting to jump us? Or does Little Turtle have another trick up his sleeve?"

Will frowned. "I do not believe Little Turtle will be the war chief of this battle. I think Blue Jacket commands the warriors."

"Good! Perhaps our chances of winning are much better then. And we must win! Do you know what this battle means to us? The whole fate of the Northwest Territory depends on what we do tomorrow. The future of the whole country is in danger.

"This battle may be our last chance. Surely, congress would never raise another army against the Indians. If we fail tomorrow, we might as well move back across the mountains. If we win, we may have a pathway clear through to the vast plains beyond. Tomorrow, we make history, one way or another. For the good of our young country, we must win!"

Will looked into the eyes of his commander and knew he meant every word he said. Still, Will felt a little guilty.

Will thought about how hard Little Turtle had fought to keep his land. He had seen his dreams crushed under the surge of settlers and soldiers. He remembered how sad the chief looked that morning he left him. Surely, Little Turtle knew that the end was near. Will would be just as glad when it was all over.

At daybreak Wayne's army marched smartly out of camp. Somewhere ahead was the enemy. No one knew where. Every soldier was on edge. The cavalry went first as an advance guard. They walked their horses and took each bend in the trail with caution.

Not far ahead 1,000 warriors were concealed in the woods. They waited on the other side of a small clearing that was snarled with fallen trees. Several years before, the spot had been hit by a cyclone.

Blue Jacket had chosen this scene for the battle because he knew the army would come upon it quickly. They wouldn't be able to get through and would come to a dead halt in full view of the hidden warriors.

Little Turtle crouched low with the other warriors. His heart was not in the battle.

Blue Jacket strutted among the warriors. "We have nothing to fear! We are in the shadow of the British fort. They have promised us help if we need it!"

Little Turtle noticed that a few British soldiers mingled with the warriors.

Impatiently, the warriors waited for the approach of Wayne's army. What is keeping them? Why aren't they here? Some warriors got tired. Others were hungry and ran behind the fort where squaws were cooking. For three days the Indians had peered through the brush waiting for the sight of the blue uniform.

About 10 o'clock the American army showed up. Major Price and his cavalry dashed out of the trees. They stopped short at the pile of timber that blocked their path. The major was bewildered.

From behind the wall of timber, shots rang out. Some men toppled from their mounts. Horses reared. Other riders galloped back through the trees. They ran right into the advancing infantry. For a moment it looked as if the whole army might turn and run.

Then through the uproar they heard General Wayne's powerful voice. "Charge!"

With a new burst of energy, the soldiers drove forward. They stumbled through and around the brush. They thrust their bayonets into Indian faces.

The warriors were surprised. They didn't have time to reload before the soldiers were upon them. They had never seen soldiers dash madly like this before. The frightened Indians ran in disorder.

Before an hour was up the Indians had fled two miles. Blue Jacket frantically tried to halt their retreat. His mouth was distorted from screaming. Time and again he rattled the dried deer hooves, the signal for attack.

Little Turtle spotted Blue Jacket through the smoke. He grabbed Blue Jacket's arm. He tore the deer hooves from his hand. "No! Run before we are all killed! Are there not enough dead warriors on the ground for you now!"

Little Turtle disappeared through the smoke. Blue Jacket stood silent for a moment in the midst of clattering guns. Then he followed Little Turtle.

General Wayne emerged from the woods just in time to see the warriors running over the meadow to the fort. Wayne wondered if the British would give the Indians shelter. If so, he would have to attack the fort.

The warriors pounded on the heavy oak doors of the fort. But they did not swing open. A red-coated sentry leaned from one of the high blockhouses. "Go on, get away! Move on!"

The warriors didn't have time to be angry with the British traitors. They fled far beyond the fort to safety. Wayne ordered his soldiers to let them go. The ground was already littered with enough warriors.

After the battle Wayne camped his army near the British fort. He eyed it with hatred. How he would like to attack it and blow it to bits. But his orders from Secretary of War Knox would not permit that.

"Well, if we can't attack the fort, there is at least one thing we can do to the British. Burn Alexander McKee's trading post! It will be his reward for urging the Indians against us!"

With heavy torches the soldiers set out and burned McKee's post and nearly everything else in sight—cornfields and vegetable gardens. For miles, one could see only scorched earth. Then the General ordered the soldiers to bury the dead. They were going back to Fort Defiance.

Wayne rode beside his captain. "I'm sure we've beaten them, Will. We lost only thirty-three men and they lost three times that many. But will they return for another fight? Are they gathering their warriors right now?"

"That's hard to tell, sir."

"There's only one way to make sure they are beaten for good. According to our orders we must destroy Kekionga. We shall put up a fort there, strong enough to instill fear in all the tribes."

Chapter XIX

A FORT AT KEKIONGA

Two months later, General Wayne and Will stood side by side inside the new fort at Kekionga. They watched a crew of soldiers firmly plant a tall flag pole in the center of the rectangle of earth.

It was October 23. The whole camp at Kekionga was bustling. Everyone was getting ready for the dedication of the fort.

"Impressive, isn't it?" Wayne commented. Will agreed. The blockhouses were made of the sturdiest oaks. Every officer and soldier had rolled up his sleeves to cut and haul the trees for the fort. They had rolled in boulders to form fireplaces. They had pieced together crude furniture. Around it all they had built a strong picket fence.

The fort stood on the most beautiful spot of Kekionga. It was where the two rivers, the St. Joseph and the St. Marys join to form the Maumee. In the background the trees were flushed with autumn. The elms were yellow. Sumacs were scarlet and maple trees were a flaming red.

The only reminder that the fort was on Indian soil were several empty houses the Indians had hastily vacated.

No one had heard much from the Indians since the battle of Fallen Timbers, as it was called. A few were seen straggling here and there. For a while there was even a rumor that they were planning another attack. General Wayne took every precaution when he marched into Kekionga, but not an Indian molested him. Too weak to resist, the Indians stood by and watched him build a fort in their capital.

"If President Washington could only see it," sighed Wayne. "This fort is something he has dreamed of for a long time!"

That afternoon General Wayne and his staff rode to the center of the fort. Troops in neat uniforms stood at attention. General Wayne boomed, "I want to thank all you men for your service to your country on the battlefield and for this great fort!"

The drums rolled. General Wayne ordered the American flag to be raised. As the flag fluttered up the pole, the troops cheered and tossed their hats into the air. Fifteen rounds of cannon fired a salute to the new fort.

Wayne then turned the fort over to its new commander, Colonel Hamtramck. Wayne twisted in his saddle and whispered to Colonel Hamtramck, "What are you going to call the new fort?"

"It seems to me there is only one thing to call it,"

Hamtramck shouted so all the men could hear. "Fort Wayne!"

The men cheered and shouted over and over, "Fort Wayne!" The general straightened in his saddle. It was easy to see he was pleased. He smiled and waved to his troops. In a way, it was a farewell. He soon had to head back to Fort Greenville. His mission in the Indian country was not quite finished. There was a treaty that had to be made. That would be the only proof that the Indians were truly resigned to peace.

Will returned with General Wayne to Fort Greenville. The general was cheered as he entered the fort. He found he was a hero all over the frontier. Settlers were rejoicing from Pittsburgh to Kentucky. President Washington and Congress sent congratulations. Wayne had won the government's first real victory over the Indians.

General Wayne settled down at Fort Greenville and waited to see what the Indians would do next.

Little Turtle heard about the white fort that stood

in his beloved Kekionga. He went to see for himself.

Unknown to white soldiers, Little Turtle hid in surrounding bushes and looked on the sturdy fort. It was a sad thing for him to see. But he knew it was there to stay. "It is like a tree with roots deep in our soil," he muttered. "We cannot go back to yesterday. We must go ahead to tomorrow. Our people are starving and cold."

Little Turtle sought out Blue Jacket. "I am going to take my people to ask for peace. I advise you to do the same."

Blue Jacket's eyes flared. He said nothing.

In January, Little Turtle sent some lesser chiefs to Fort Wayne with a white flag to ask the white chief to talk peace. Hamtramck relayed the message to General Wayne. Wayne invited the chiefs of all tribes to meet at Fort Greenville in the summer.

On June 16, 1795, General Wayne kindled the council fire at Fort Greenville. He still wasn't certain the Indians really wanted peace. He wondered if their actions were a trick. He also heard rumors that Little Turtle and Blue Jacket would not show up for the council.

Several hundred Indians straggled into Fort Greenville. They camped on the outskirts of the fort. They were a sad procession. Most were starved, their faces gaunt from hunger. They had had a hard winter. General Wayne gave them food while they waited for other chiefs to come.

Days passed. Little Turtle did not appear.

Every day Will scouted the forest looking for his Indian father. He questioned arriving warriors. He could learn nothing.

Wayne was troubled. "Will Little Turtle come? We can do nothing without him. For he is still the leader of the confederated tribes. Most warriors regret that they did not listen to Little Turtle instead of Blue Jacket. Then there would have been no battle at Fallen Timbers."

"He will come," said Will. "I know he will come."

On an afternoon in early July, Will heard a commotion among the tribes camped near the fort. He dashed to the lookout and peered down. There, striding along the dusty path toward the fort gate was Little Turtle. Close behind was a delegation of Miami warriors.

Will never failed to be amazed by Little Turtle. He was a defeated war chief who had just lost his home, his land, his heritage. Yet, he did not hang his head. His shoulders were thrown back. His dark eyes pointed straight ahead. He looked more like a victorious war chief coming to claim his prize.

Will scrambled down from the lookout and sprinted to the front gate. The doors swung inward. Will stood face to face with Little Turtle. The chief's eyes looked deep into Will's. Then the arms of Little Turtle came up to Will's shoulders.

"How good it is to see you again," said Will. He knew Little Turtle felt the same, although he did not speak at once.

General Wayne in cocked hat and dress uniform strode forth to greet Little Turtle. Will translated the general's greetings to Little Turtle. "This is General Wayne. He welcomes you to the council and is very glad you came."

Little Turtle and General Wayne studied each other. Two great warriors from different races had at last come face to face. Little Turtle spoke to Will. "It is not surprising that such a man has taken our land and killed our strongest warriors. We shall talk peace whenever he is ready."

More than 1,000 Indians finally showed up at Fort Greenville. Blue Jacket was among them.

On July 20, the great chiefs entered the long council house. General Wayne and his aides sat together. Captain Wells sat next to the general to interpret the Indian tongues. Squatted all around the soldiers were chiefs of the Miamis, Shawnees, Delawares, Wyandots, Ottawas, Chippewas and Potawatomis.

General Wayne started the discussion. It was clear

that he had the upper hand. After all, he was the victor. Little Turtle knew his people were doomed. They didn't have much ground on which to argue.

Yet, Little Turtle did his best. He fought hard to retain as much Indian land as possible. He sat silent while more and more land passed into the white man's hands.

At last, he stood in all his splendor. His nose jewels sparkled and his long earrings jingled. He addressed General Wayne, "Kekionga has been our home forever. Grant us a reservation there."

The general refused. "Every fort has a right to reserve as much land for itself as its cannons can shoot. It is impossible to grant your wish.

"However, I have goods worth $20,000 for your people and I promise to deliver $9,500 more each year forever. The government also offers you $1,000 for a new log home and $1,200 to buy tools to turn your people to farming. For they must find other ways to make a living."

That was it. Nothing Little Turtle said made any difference. The boundary lines were soon drawn. The Indians were allowed to keep only one-third of the upper Ohio country.

On August 3, 1795, a dozen or more chiefs filed up to General Wayne's desk to sign the Treaty of Greenville. Last, Little Turtle stepped forward and put his sign on the sheet of paper.

General Wayne then said farewell to the congregation of Indians: "I now pray to the Great Spirit that the peace may hold us together in friendship until time shall be no more.

"I also pray that the Great Spirit above may enlighten your minds and open your eyes to your true happiness that your children may learn to cultivate the earth and enjoy the fruits of peace. I bid you an affectionate farewell and wish you a safe and happy return to your respective homes and families."

Little Turtle approached General Wayne and Will who stood together.

"I have been the last to sign the treaty," said Little Turtle quietly. "I shall be the last to break it." Will translated the words. General Wayne nodded politely.

Captain Wells looked fondly at the brown, worn face of Chief Little Turtle. The chief's eyes were still burning. Will knew that kind of fire would never go out. They burned as brightly as ever, even after his whole Indian nation had burned out.

Will turned abruptly to General Wayne. "Sir, I would like to become an agent at Fort Wayne. Now that we are at peace, I would like to return there with my Indian father."

General Wayne was slightly surprised. "I guess it could be arranged. We shall need an Indian agent there. Yes, go ahead, if you want."

Little Turtle could not tell what the two men were talking about. He understood only after Will took his arm and led him away from the crowd. Together they rode out of Fort Greenville, Wells to Kekionga and Little Turtle to his village.

Chapter XX

THE LAST WHISPER

After the Treaty of Greenville, Little Turtle was a war chief no more. He carefully removed the eagle feather from his scalp lock. He let his hair grow long and gray over his shoulders.

He drew his tomahawk from his belt and hung it on the wall of his home. He let his gun stand in the corner. Sometimes he picked it up and wiped the dust from the barrel.

Then he remembered how he had been a great war

chief. He entertained his grandchildren with tales of the great battles he had led. He did not regret his war years, nor did he yearn for them.

He often told Will, "I was born to be a war chief. Today my people no longer need a war chief. War has disappeared like the buffalo from Kekionga. It is a time of peace."

Little Turtle meant what he said. He fought for his people in time of peace, as he had done in war.

For years he traveled, talking to his people and urging them to farm. Three times he journeyed to Philadelphia. The first time he met with President Washington to ask help in teaching farming to the tribes.

President Washington was quite impressed with the war chief who had twice outwitted American generals. The President gave Little Turtle a medal and a splendid sword which the chief prized very highly.

Later Little Turtle visited both President Adams and President Jefferson to beg for laws to keep whiskey from his people.

Even when he was an old man Little Turtle's energy did not seem to dwindle. But more and more he enjoyed just lying in the yard of his home, looking up at the tall trees.

When Will asked what he was doing, he replied he was listening to the wind. "What does it say?" Will asked one summer day in 1812. Little Turtle closed his lips. He would speak no more about it. "Nothing you would want to hear, my son."

A few days later Little Turtle died on July 14, 1812, at the age of 61.

He was buried as he had lived—like a great warrior. The United States Army gave their former enemy a final tribute—a military funeral.

That day it was unbearably hot. The sun burned on a crowd of Indians waiting outside the heavy gate of Fort Wayne.

In a moment, the doors opened and six soldiers in full dress uniform appeared. On their strong shoulders rested a wooden casket containing the body of Little

Turtle. Behind them came a corps of drummers beating lightly on muffled drums. Then came horses pulling a cannon—then more men.

The file of soldiers turned sharply to the right and marched solemnly out of Kekionga. The crowd of mourning Indians fell in behind. The procession stopped at a gaping grave in William Wells' orchard.

Gently the soldiers let Little Turtle's body into the black moist grave. Then they dropped in his necklaces, bracelets, his tomahawk and the treasured sword President Washington had given him.

The soldiers stood back at attention. The cannon boomed a last salute into the hot air. All was silent. Then as if in echo, a slight wind slipped down out of the apple trees and rustled the grass near the open grave.

IMPORTANT DATES

Birth of Little Turtle	1751
George Rogers Clark took Kaskaskia	1778
Clark took Vincennes	1779
LaBalme Massacre	1780
Northwest Territory created; Marietta, Ohio, settled	1787
Fort Washington built (Cincinnati)	1789
George Washington became President	1789
General Harmar's defeat	1790
Fort Hamilton built (Hamilton, Ohio)	1791
Fort Jefferson built	1791
General St. Clair's defeat	1791
Fort Greenville built (Greenville, Ohio)	1793
Fort Recovery built	1793
Fort Adams, Fort Defiance, Fort Deposit built	1794

Battle of Fallen Timbers	1794
Fort Wayne built (Fort Wayne, Indiana)	1794
Treaty of Greenville	1795
Indiana Territory formed	1800
Ohio became a state	1803
Death of Chief Little Turtle	1812